CUSTOMARY U.S. MEASURES AND EQUIVALENTS

METRIC MEASURES AND EQUIVALENTS

LENGTH

1 inch (in)		= 2.54 cm
1 foot (ft)	= 12 in	= .3048 m
1 yard (yd)	= 3 ft	= .9144 m
1 mile (mi)	= 1760 yd	= 1.6093 km
1 nautical mile	= 1.152 mi	= 1.853 km

1 millimeter (mm)		= .0394 in
1 centimeter (cm)	= 10 mm	= .3937 in
1 meter (m)	= 1000 mm	= 1.0936 yd
1 kilometer (km)	= 1000 m	= .6214 mi

AREA

1 square inch (in^2)		= 6.4516 cm^2
1 square foot (ft^2)	= 144 in^2	= .093 m^2
1 square yard (yd^2)	= 9 ft^2	= .8361 m^2
1 acre	= 4840 yd^2	= 4046.86 m^2
1 square mile(mi^2)	= 640 acre	= 2.59 km^2

1 sq centimeter (cm^2)	= 100 mm^2	= .155 in^2
1 sq meter (m^2)	= 10,000 cm^2	= 1.196 yd^2
1 hectare (ha)	= 10,000 m^2	= 2.4711 acres
1 sq kilometer (km^2)	= 100 ha	= .3861 mi^2

WEIGHT

1 ounce (oz)	= 437.5 grains	= 28.35 g
1 pound (lb)	= 16 oz	= .4536 kg
1 short ton	= 2000 lb	= .9072 t
1 long ton	= 2240 lb	= 1.0161 t

1 milligram (mg)		= .0154 grain
1 gram (g)	= 1000 mg	= .0353 oz
1 kilogram (kg)	= 1000 g	= 2.2046 lb
1 tonne (t)	= 1000 kg	= 1.1023 short tons
1 tonne		= .9842 long ton

VOLUME

1 cubic inch (in^3)		= 16.387 cm^3
1 cubic foot (ft^3)	= 1728 in^3	= .028 m^3
1 cubic yard (yd^3)	= 27 ft^3	= .7646 m^3
1 fluid ounce (fl oz)		= 2.957 cl
1 liquid pint (pt)	= 16 fl oz	= .4732 l
1 liquid quart (qt)	= 2 pt	= .946 l
1 gallon (gal)	= 4 qt	= 3.7853 l
1 dry pint		= .5506 l
1 bushel (bu)	= 64 dry pt	= 35.2381 l

1 cubic centimeter (cm^3)		= .061 in^3
1 cubic decimeter (dm^3)	= 1000 cm^3	= .353 ft^3
1 cubic meter (m^3)	= 1000 dm^3	= 1.3079 yd^3
1 liter (l)	= 1 dm^3	= .2642 gal
1 hectoliter (hl)	= 100 l	= 2.8378 bu

TEMPERATURE

CELSIUS° = 5/9 (F° − 32°)   FAHRENHEIT° = 9/5 C° + 32°

JURASSIC FISHES

Translated by Christopher Perrius

HARUTO KODERA

Toshiaki Igarashi
Nobuhito Kuroiwa
Hiroshi Maeda
Shinya Mitani
Fumitoshi Mori
Koichi Yamazaki

PHOTOS BY RYU UCHIYAMA

Distributed in the UNITED STATES to the Pet Trade by T.F.H. Publications, Inc., One T.F.H. Plaza, Neptune City, NJ 07753; distributed in the UNITED STATES to the Bookstore and Library Trade by National Book Network, Inc. 4720 Boston Way, Lanham MD 20706; in CANADA to the Pet Trade by H & L Pet Supplies Inc., 27 Kingston Crescent, Kitchener, Ontario N2B 2T6; Rolf C. Hagen Ltd., 3225 Sartelon Street, Montreal 382 Quebec; in CANADA to the Book Trade by Macmillan of Canada (A Division of Canada Publishing Corporation), 164 Commander Boulevard, Agincourt, Ontario M1S 3C7; in ENGLAND by T.F.H. Publications, PO Box 15, Waterlooville PO7 6BQ; in AUSTRALIA AND THE SOUTH PACIFIC by T.F.H. (Australia), Pty. Ltd., Box 149, Brookvale 2100 N.S.W., Australia; in NEW ZEALAND by Brooklands Aquarium Ltd. 5 McGiven Drive, New Plymouth, RD1 New Zealand; in Japan by T.F.H. Publications, Japan—Jiro Tsuda, 10-12-3 Ohjidai, Sakura, Chiba 285, Japan; in SOUTH AFRICA by Multipet Pty. Ltd., P.O. Box 35347, Northway, 4065, South Africa. Published by T.F.H. Publications, Inc.
MANUFACTURED IN THE UNITED STATES OF AMERICA
BY T.F.H. PUBLICATIONS, INC.

Originally published in Japanese by Marine Publishing Co. under the title *Ancient Fish*. © 1992 by M.P.J.

CONTENTS

A GLIMPSE INTO OUR DISTANT EVOLUTIONARY PAST

by Haruto Kodera
Tsurumi University Dental College, Anatomy Department

When you look at a primitive fish in an aquarium, you are looking deep into the wondrous past of life on earth. Primitive fishes came into being in the Upper Cambrian period some 500 million years ago. We know that the climate was very different then from now. The Northern Hemisphere of Earth was hot and dry, while the Southern Hemisphere was cool. Widespread layers of red earth called "old red sandstone" indicate that the Atlantic coastal plain that stretched from present-day Scotland to northwestern Europe was tropical. Sandwiched in this layer of oxidized earth are layers of green mud that are rich in fish fossils.

A person traveling west through Europe in the Ordovician and Silurian periods would have had to cross a great desert before reaching the fertile coastal region, where he or she would find the beginnings of forests with ferns growing beside lakes and ponds. These bodies of fresh water were the hothouses of ancient fish evolution, from the oldest vertebrates, the Agnatha (jawless fishes), to the armor-plated placoderms and arthrodirans and the teleosts.

Not only fishes thrived in these waters, but also aquatic scorpions and insects, mollusks, and many other invertebrates that have left fossils behind. In stark contrast to the rather barren continent, the water was home to a growing variety of fishes and other animals. Only a few of the great number of species from this time have continued their lines until today, among them the lungfishes, bichirs, and the coelacanth.

Living lungfishes are presently found on only three continents of the Southern Hemisphere (Africa, South America, and Australia), but we know that they lived all over the world in the Mesozoic era. They are the best-known primitive fishes, with the telltale characteristics of well-developed lungs (more developed than amphibians), a body with scales, frog-like eggs, and a primitive appearance.

However, the classification of the lungfishes is the focus of fierce debate among taxonomists. It used to be generally believed that *Osteolepis* was the common ancestor of the Coelacanthiformes and lungfishes, and the Coelacanthiformes then developed into *Eusthenopteron* and the amphibians. But recently it has been argued that the lungfishes are closely related to the early amphibians, and another theory claims that the lungfish is the missing link to the sea for land animals. Now, most scientists agree that all of these groups are directly descended from *Osteolepis*: first the lungfishes, next the Coelacanthiformes, then finally the amphibians and the closely related *Eusthenopteron*.

One large debate is centered on the question of the internal nostril. The lungfishes, coelacanth, and *Osteolepis* were grouped together on the basis of their sharing that characteristic. Then it was learned that the coelacanth doesn't have one, and the lungfish's internal nostril may possibly not be a true one. The whole practice of grouping fishes by the presence or absence of the internal nostril has been called into question.

As they entered the Devonian period, important specializations were already taking place in the lungfishes: the pointed tip of the skull disappeared, and its teeth became fixed into ridged bony plates. The powerful bite, on the other hand, is the result of a skull and muscle structure that is common to the coelacanth and bichirs.

Another fish line that has survived since the Mesozoic era is that of *Polypterus*. Fossils of it have been found only in layers from the Cretaceous period onward, but since its structure has strong resemblances to primitive teleosts, it is considered to be early Mesozoic in origin. The characteristics of such fishes are

Arapaima gigas is one of the largest freshwater fishes in the world. Photo from a Manaus telephone book cover.

in other ways, i.e., by developing sturdier skeletons and greater mobility. Of the chondrosteans that dominated the Mesozoic era, only *Amia* and the gars remain.

Around the end of the Mesozoic era, during that period of so-called evolutionary trial and error when a mind-boggling variety of unusual kinds of fishes appeared, we find the teleosts. One of these groups is the Osteoglossiformes. The abundant fossils of the *Lycoptera* in China are a well-known instance. The modern-day *Arapaima* is considered more toward the end of this primitive line. Variations exist among these, such as electric organs, as in the tail of the elephant-nose fishes, and spiral intestines. These fishes already have a modern air about them.

Primitive fishes are relics that have been crucial to the understanding of the evolution of fishes and higher vertebrates such as ourselves. The morphologist Shigeo Mitsugi claims that among deformities of human pulmonary veins are examples of the lung structures of primitive fishes like *Polypterus* and *Amia*. The mysteries of the origin of the human body were first unraveled through observation of and research on primitive fishes. Even though there are no direct ancestors among existing prehistoric fishes, in their various physical structures we can catch glimpses of humanity's evolutionary origins.

Why have these primitive fishes survived until today? There is no simple answer, but one important

thick, ganoid scales, a large gular plate, exterior gills in the young, and a pair of lungs, one on each side of the trunk, as in humans.

The genealogical position of *Polypterus* is also hotly debated. Some say it belongs in the Actinopterygii, others in the Brachyopterygii, or between the Brachyopterygii and the sturgeons. *Polypterus* itself probably belongs to the group of the most primitive of the sturgeons.

One of the mysteries of *Polypterus* is that both fossils and modern species are found only in Africa. The key to the riddle of its origin is certainly to be found somewhere in West Africa.

The Mesozoic era was a stable one in comparison to the following Cenozoic era, our era, which has been marked by violent changes in the earth's crust. Most of the planet's climate was tropical, and the representative fishes of that time were the chondrosteans, the predecessor of today's sturgeons. Fishes like *Polypterus*, which have retained Paleozoic characteristics such as ganoid scales and functioning lungs, have improved

The coelacanths were thought to have become extinct 70-80 million years ago, but a live specimen was trawled in 1938 and eventually named *Latimeria chalumnae*.

Dr. Herbert R. Axelrod proudly holding the head of a fossilized coelacanth that was named after him, *Axelrodichthys araripensis*. The fossil came from the Santana Formation of northeastern Brazil and is thought to be approximately 110 million years old. For a full story of this exciting find see *T.F.H.* magazine for May, 1986, and November, 1987.

reason is that climatic conditions that existed in the Mesozoic and even Paleozoic eras can still be found in some places today.

Raising primitive fishes may look easy, but there are all sorts of pitfalls to avoid. I hope this book will guide you safely through whatever difficulties you may encounter.

Of the chondrosteans that dominated the Mesozoic era, only the gars and this species, *Amia calva*, remain today. Photo by Ken Lucas, Steinhart Aquarium.

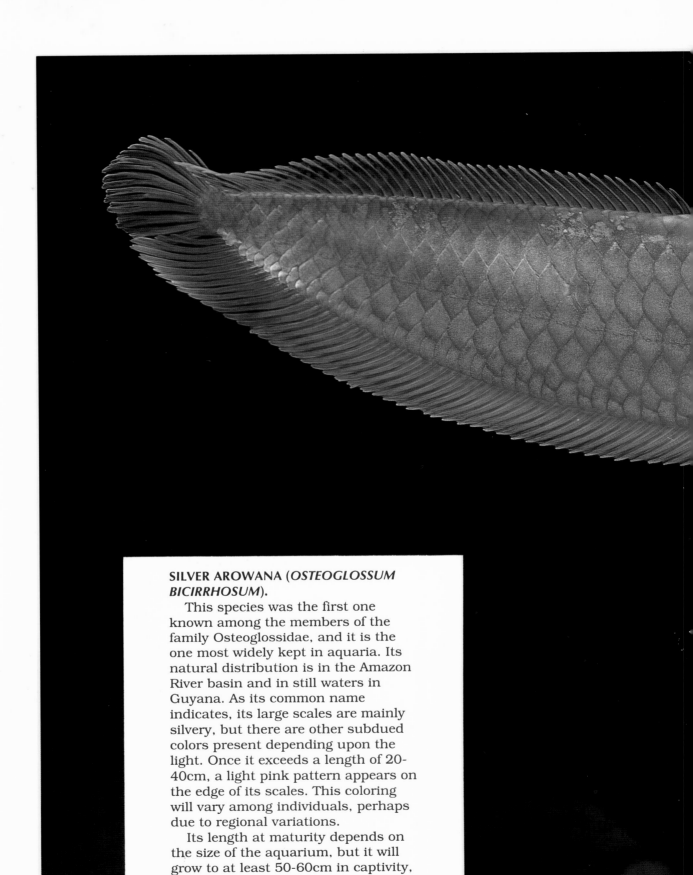

SILVER AROWANA (*OSTEOGLOSSUM BICIRRHOSUM*).

This species was the first one known among the members of the family Osteoglossidae, and it is the one most widely kept in aquaria. Its natural distribution is in the Amazon River basin and in still waters in Guyana. As its common name indicates, its large scales are mainly silvery, but there are other subdued colors present depending upon the light. Once it exceeds a length of 20-40cm, a light pink pattern appears on the edge of its scales. This coloring will vary among individuals, perhaps due to regional variations.

Its length at maturity depends on the size of the aquarium, but it will grow to at least 50-60cm in captivity, and wild specimens are known to exceed one meter in length. Arowanas of the genus *Osteoglossum* have longer dorsal and anal fin bases than arowanas of the genus *Scleropages*.

If it can become accustomed to the local water conditions the Silver Arowana is a hardy species that will grow 30cm or more in its first six months. It is a mouthbrooder that has been successfully bred in Japan, where it is also an important food fish. Every year large numbers of young bearing yolk sacs are imported into Japan between October and March, but, perhaps because they are cheaper than other arowanas, they are often roughly handled. It will certainly continue to be a valuable fish, so it should be properly cared for. With good treatment, an arowana will be as beautiful a specimen as any other fish in the aquarium.

Top: A young Silver Arowana with its yolk sac still very obvious. **Bottom:** A young Silver Arowana at home in a suitably spacious aquarium.

Top: The arowana's upward slanting lower jaw is one of its distinguishing characteristics. **Bottom:** Arowanas of the genus *Osteoglossum* have very limber bodies and can turn very quickly.

BLACK AROWANA (*OSTEOGLOSSUM FERREIRAI*)

This rarer arowana is native to the Rio Branco, a tributary of the Rio Negro in northwestern Brazil. It has been imported into Japan since 1967, but in lesser numbers than its silvery cousin. Young with yolk sacs still attached to their bellies are imported from November to April.

The Black Arowana very closely resembles the Silver Arowana, except that its body is less deep, and the number of scales in the lateral line, the number of dorsal and anal fin rays, and the number of vertebrae are all higher in the Black Arowana.

Aquarium-raised specimens will attain lengths of 30-40cm or more, while wild ones have been said to grow to more than 60cm in length. It is more nervous than other arowanas, and more finicky about its diet.

When young, the Black Arowana has a relatively broad, cream-colored stripe running from its barbels through its eyes to its tail, but after growing to a size of around 10cm its color gradually changes to gray and this stripe fades away. Then its fins and individual scales become bordered in pink and indigo. This color change is extremely delicate and a beautiful process to watch in carefully-raised specimens.

Arowanas are laterally compressed, which can be seen when viewed head on. Even large specimens can swim easily through relatively narrow spaces.

A mature Black Arowana. Note the extreme color change in this species as it grows.

A young Black Arowana bearing a yolk sac that is almost depleted.

Golden Arowana (Asian Arowana).

ASIAN AROWANA (*SCLEROPAGES FORMOSUS*)

Native to the gentle currents of Malaysia and Indonesia, it is said that the Asian Arowana does not appear in the mountains or lowlands. This arowana used to be divided by its color variations into the Red Arowana, the Green Arowana, and so on, but since the form and behavior of all of these color morphs are the same, they are treated as a single species.

Among ethnic Chinese merchants the Asian Arowana is considered a lucky fish and it is nicknamed the "Red Dragon" and the "Prosperity Fish." In Japan it is called the "Illusory Arowana," and it has been imported there since 1971.

There are two Australian arowanas of the genus *Scleropages*, but they differ from the Asian species in the

Golden Arowana (Asian Arowana).

12

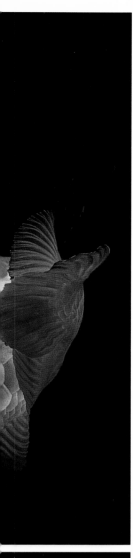

Golden Arowana (Asian Arowana).

Green Arowana (Asian Arowana).

Green Arowana (Asian Arowana).

number of scales in the lateral line; they have 32-35 while the Asian Arowana has 21-25. They are commonly referred to as Barramundis, a common name also shared by *Lates* in Australia.

The Asian Arowana is a mouthbrooder that can carry 30-80 eggs in its mouth, and it has been successfully bred in Japan recently.

In Appendix I of CITES, it is listed as a highest-level protected fish, and annual limits on imports were agreed upon at the 1989 Rosanne Conference. (Maeda)

Blood-red Dragon (Asian Arowana).

Orange Arowana (Asian Arowana).

Orange Arowana (Asian Arowana).

Orange Arowana (Asian Arowana).

Although all the arowanas on the last few pages are variously colored (like this Orange Arowana), they are all specimens of the Asian Arowana.

Above: A mature Northern Barramundi. **Below:** A young Northern Barramundi (6 cm long).

NORTHERN BARRAMUNDI (*SCLEROPAGES JARDINII*)

This species is found in northern Australia from the Jardine River of the Cape York Peninsula to the Adelaide River near Darwin, as well as in the rivers that flow into the Timor Sea and the Gulf of Carpentaria, where it is locally called the Gulf Saratoga. This same pure freshwater species is also found in the rivers of New Guinea.

S. jardinii is greenish brown dorsally and light brown or green-gray on its sides, with silver scales usually with a red or pink crescent-moon pattern.

It inhabits still waters or those with gentle currents, and spawns when the water reaches about 30°C, sometime between September and November in northern Australia. It is a mouthbrooder that can carry some 30-130 eggs at a time. The eggs hatch in one to two weeks, after which the young are protected in the mother's mouth for another four to five weeks. When they leave the mother's mouth, the young are 3.5-4cm long, and grow to 10cm in about three months.

The Northern Barramundi is a favorite with anglers for its fight and for its flavor. Weights of one or two kilograms are common, but in Dr. G. Allen's book, *Freshwater Fishes of Australia*, published by T.F.H. Publications, Inc., a 27kg specimen was recorded.

SPOTTED BARRAMUNDI (*SCLEROPAGES LEICHARDTI*)

The Spotted Barramundi, also known as the Saratoga in its native area, is found wild in the Fitzroy River system of Queensland in eastern Australia, although several other rivers have been stocked with it. It normally grows to a length of about 50cm, but it can reach 90cm in length. It prefers still waters or those with gentle currents, and it is often found near shore where there is heavy vegetation. It spawns in November and December before the rainy season begins.

Its back is a dark brown or bluish olive, and its sides are a bright silver. There is a spotted pattern on its scales, hence its name. This pattern is the best way to distinguish it from the Northern Barramundi.

The Spotted Barramundi's diet consists of beetles, small fishes, frogs, crayfish, and other crustaceans. It can reportedly live in water temperatures of up to 40°C. A highly territorial fish, it will viciously fight with others of its kind.

A young Spotted Barramundi (12 cm long).

A lake where Spotted Barramundi have been caught.

A mature Spotted Barramundi caught by an angler. Photo by Kiyoshi Sakurai.

A mature Pirarucu (*Arapaima gigas*). Note the red markings on its posterior flanks.

A young Pirarucu (10 cm long).

PIRARUCU (*ARAPAIMA GIGAS*)

Arapaima gigas is one of the largest freshwater fishes in the world, reaching lengths of 4.5-5m and weights of 200kg. It ranges from the Amazon River basin through the Orinoco River basin to parts of Guyana. It has long been an important part of the native diet, and its scales and tongue are used as files and other tools. Harpooning was a common fishing method. However, it has been overfished lately with nets and more modern equipment, and specimens over 2m long have become rare.

Its mouth is large for its relatively small head, and its laterally flattened, deep body is covered with large, hard scales. The dorsal and anal fins are roughly the same length, about a third the length of its body. The young are a blackish olive, but as they mature Pirarucus develop a red coloring on the edges of their scales that

contrasts vividly with the dull olive background.

The Pirarucu feeds on fishes by first getting close to its prey, then suddenly opening its mouth so that the fish will be sucked in along with the inrushing water to be swallowed whole. In captivity it also prefers live fishes (goldfish, etc.), but it can be trained to eat artificial foods or dead fishes. It is actually a relatively light eater.

It grows extremely quickly. A 15cm juvenile will reach 60cm in a year and one meter in three years. For this reason it is more suitable to a public aquarium than a private home. Ideal water conditions are 25°C, low to medium acidity, and somewhat aged water, but the Pirarucu is pretty flexible. (Mitani)

A young African Arowana (*Heterotis niloticus*).

A mature African Arowana. This species is often also called the Nile Arowana.

AFRICAN AROWANA (*HETEROTIS NILOTICUS*)

As the name *niloticus* suggests, this species is native to the Nile River system as well as the Niger River basin. Due to its resemblance to the arowanas, it is called the African or Nile Arowana, but it is in fact a member of the subfamily that includes the Pirarucu.

It grows to a length of 90cm, and its gray scales are quite a bit smaller than those of the arowanas. Sometimes there are markings on the fish's side that look very much like an injury.

The African Arowana has a large, oblique, protractile mouth. It feeds on plankton by filtering it through its gill rakers. In the aquarium it will eat bloodworms, tubificid worms, and finely ground artificial food. It is important to feed this fish at least twice a day.

H. niloticus has a generally mild disposition, but some specimens are aggressive and will fight their own and other species. Of course, since it doesn't eat other fishes, it can be kept with relatively small fishes such as some of the plecos.

In its native waters it builds a large nest among plants for spawning, and the male and female watch over the eggs together. (Maeda)

The "facial" features of this Butterfly Fish are similar to those of the arowanas.

A mature Butterfly Fish, *Pantodon buchholzi.*

BUTTERFLY FISH (*PANTODON BUCHHOLZI*)

The Butterfly Fish is silvery or greenish brown with irregular brown spots and/or stripes. All of the rays of the fins are marked by an alternating dark and light pattern that forms stripes or bands across the fin. A dark band encircles the front of the head, cutting across the eye to the lower jaw.

Pantodon is native to the still waters of tropical regions of West Africa, Niger, Zaire, Cameroon, and elsewhere. It has an upward opening jaw and a short, compact body, and it can leap a meter or more out of the water to catch insects. However, it doesn't flutter around like a South American hatchetfish.

Its dorsal fin is located far posteriorly and is very small, but the pectoral fin is large and well developed. The long pelvic fin filaments are provided with sensory organs. The swim bladder is highly vascularized and can utilize oxygen from the air.

Males and females can be distinguished by the shape of the anal fin: a straight edged anal fin indicates it is a female, and an uneven one indicates it is a male. Not much is known about its behavior in the wild, but it seems to subsist mainly on surface insects and small fishes. (Maeda)

ABA ABA (*GYMNARCHUS NILOTICUS*)

Gymnarchus niloticus is found in, of course, the Nile River, as well as the Niger, Senegal, and Gambia Rivers, and Lakes Rudolf (Lake Turkana) and Chad. It grows to 15cm or more. In 1829, the great French scholar Georges Cuvier of the Museum d'Histoire naturelle d'Paris described this species, which is monotypic (having a single family, genus, and species).

Its most striking characteristic is its highly developed dorsal fin, which enables it to swim gracefully and with great beauty.

When mature specimens were first imported some twenty years ago they could cost upwards of $5000, but they are now bred in captivity and young ones have become available and affordable.

The Aba Aba is extremely aggressive and should never be kept with other fishes, including its own kind. It generally feeds on small fishes, but young ones can be fed frozen or live bloodworms. It grows quickly and lives long. All in all, it is a very resilient fish and therefore easy to raise if you don't mind its nasty personality. (Igarashi)

A young Aba Aba (7 cm).

An albino Aba Aba.

A mature Aba Aba.

Peter's Elephantnose, *Gnathonemus petersii*.

PETER'S ELEPHANTNOSE (*GNATHONEMUS PETERSII*)

The most famous species in the family Mormyridae is not in the genus *Mormyrus* but this species of the genus *Gnathonemus*. Elephantnoses are found in many parts of Africa, including the Congo (Zaire), Lake Victoria, Nigeria and Cameroon. Its "trunk" is actually its lower lip, which it uses to hunt for small organisms in the muddy lake bottom. It grows to about 20cm.

STANLEY FALLS ELEPHANTNOSE (*MARCUSENIUS STANLEYANUS*)

At first glance this species appears rather different from its cousin, but the swollen lower mental area gives it away. It is also a mid-sized fish of about 20cm, and it is native to the Zaire basin. A very similar species, *M. senegalensis*, is found in Senegal and Togo.

Stanley Falls Elephantnose, *Marcusenius stanleyanus*.

24

Above: A birdbeak elephantnose, *Campylomormyrus* sp. **Center:** The Ibis Elephantnose, *Campylomormyrus ibis.* **Bottom:** Another species of birdbeak elephantnose, *Campylomormyrus* sp.

BIRDBEAK ELEPHANTNOSES (*CAMPYLOMORMYRUS* SPP.)

Several species of this genus go by the common name "birdbeak elephantnoses," which refers, of course, to their extended snouts. *C. ibis* is also called the Longnose Birdbeak Elephantnose, an even crueler appellation. They all grow to about 15cm. These long-nosed mormyrids are generally found in the Zaire system. *C. numenius* is another well-known species.

A doubletrunk elephantnose, *Campylomormyrus* sp.

A doubletrunk elephantnose, *Campylomormyrus* sp.

DOUBLETRUNK ELEPHANTNOSES (*CAMPYLOMORMYRUS* SPP.)

Many closely related *Campylomormyrus* species are also sold under the common name "doubletrunk elephantnoses," including *C. mirus* and *C. tamandua*. *C. elephas*, native to the upper basin of the Zaire River, is a popular doubletrunk elephantnose. It grows to 15cm in captivity but 40cm specimens have been captured. It is territorial and will fight fiercely with any other doubletrunk elephantnose that intrudes.

Above: A doubletrunk elephantnose, *Campylomormyrus* sp. **Right:** Donkeyfaced Elephantnose, *Campylomormyrus cassaicus*.

DONKEYFACED ELEPHANTNOSE (*CAMPYLOMORMYRUS CASSAICUS*)

This fish has a face that only a mother could love but that everyone can easily recognize. Its long "nose" is sharply angled to point nearly straight down, and its round head rises to slightly above its back. It occurs in the Zaire River. Unlike most of the mormyrids it does not hide in the shadows, so it is an excellent fish for the aquarium. It grows to about 15cm.

26

NORTH AFRICAN WHALE (*PETROCEPHALUS BANE*)

This mormyrid is distinguished by its sharply slender caudal peduncle, its rounded snout, and the nearly exact match between the base lengths of its dorsal and anal fins. (A more famous mormyrid with a rounded snout is the 10cm *Pollimyrus isidori*.) It is widely distributed in North Africa, including Lake Chad and the Nile and Niger Rivers. It reaches a length of about 20cm. (Mori)

DOMODOMO (*MORMYRUS KANNUME*)

This species is the most common of the dolphin mormyrids, and its shape and large size (50cm and up) do give it a resemblance to the popular mammals. Other closely-related species are also sold under that name, however. All dolphin mormyrids are large, and will eat killifishes as well as bloodworms. The Domodomo is found in the Nile basin and Lake Victoria.

Top: North African Whale, *Petrocephalus bane*. **Above:** Domodomo, *Mormyrus kannume*.

WHALE ELEPHANTNOSE (*BRIENOMYRUS BRACHYISTIUS*)

The Whale Elephantnose is distributed over a wide range from Zaire to Sierra Leone. Although there are other species that go by this name in the aquarium trade, this one is the most popular. The base of the anal fin is approximately twice the length of the base of the dorsal fin, its snout is rounded, and there is no jaw protrusion. Its color varies from gray to dark brown, and it reaches a length of about 17cm. The Whale Elephantnose is rarely collected and imported into Japan. (Mori)

SPECKLED ELEPHANTNOSE (*POLYMYRUS LHUYSII*)

This species is found in the Senegal area. Its color is unique for a mormyrid, dark brown speckles on a silvery brown background. The anal fin base length is about 1.5 times that of the dorsal base. The genus is spreading out across tropical Africa from the Nile River system. (Mori)

LONG-FINNED ELEPHANTNOSE (*BRIENOMYRUS LONGIANALIS*)

This long-bodied type, whose length is five times its height, is native to the Niger River basin. It is characterized by the large eyes and large gape. The anal fin length to dorsal fin length ratio is about three to one. It grows to about 15cm and is rarely imported into Japan.

From Top to Bottom: The Whale Elephantnose, *Brienomyrus brachyistius*. The Speckled Elephantnose, *Polymyrus lhuysii*. The Long-finned Elephantnose, *Brienomyrus longianalis*.

TRUMPET MORMYRID (*MORMYROPS ZANCLIROSTRIS*)

This long-nosed mormyrid is found in the Zaire River area and grows to 30cm. Another species of *Mormyrops*, *M. boulengeri*, has the same type of "nose" but it is longer. Its eyes are very small even for the poor-sighted mormyrid family, and so it must be strictly nocturnal. It is slow-moving but quick to fight.

TORPEDO MORMYRID (*MORMYROPS ENGYSTOMA*)

This species' snout protrudes but slightly, yet it belongs to the same genus, *Mormyrops*, as the fish above. The distinguishing characteristic of this genus is the length of the anal fin (or to be exact, the length of the base of the anal fin), which is about twice that of the dorsal fin. *M. engystoma* inhabits the lower Zaire River basin, and is 15cm at maturity. It tends to get thin when domesticated, so it requires careful feeding.

SMALL DORSAL ELEPHANTNOSE (*HYPEROPISUS BEBE*)

This species is included in its own genus, but this is not uncommon in the family Mormyridae. It is distinguished by its long anal fin base, 3-5 times longer than that of the dorsal. Its snout is short, and the lower jaw protrudes slightly. Specimens of 46cm length have been reported in the wild. It is rarely imported into Japan.

From Top to Bottom: The Trumpet Mormyrid, *Mormyrops zanclirostris*. An albino Torpedo Mormyrid, *Mormyrops engystoma*. The Small Dorsal Elephantnose, *Hyperopisus bebe*. A yellow Small Dorsal Elephantnose.

ROYAL KNIFE FISH (*CHITALA BLANCI*)

The Royal Knife Fish is a relative newcomer among knife fishes, but it has been imported in larger quantities in recent years and has become fairly familiar to Japanese aquarists. It ranges throughout Cambodia and Thailand, and grows to over 80cm in length. It is a real beauty, with a shiny silver or gold body and dark stripes on its posterior half. Like the Spotted Knife Fish, its distinguishing marks appear as it matures.

Below: The Royal Knife Fish, *Chitala blanci*.

SPOTTED OR CLOWN KNIFE FISH (*CHITALA ORNATA*)

This species was long known as *Notopterus chitala*, but its generic placement was recently reevaluated (Roberts, 1992). It is the most common of the knife fishes, and it is distributed all over southern and southeastern Asia. There have been specimens captured that were a meter long. It is an important food fish, and usually the flesh is thoroughly dried before eaten. It is aggressive toward its own kind.

Left: The Spotted Knife Fish, *Chitala ornata*. **Below, top**: An albino Spotted Knife Fish. **Below, bottom:** A young Spotted Knife Fish (6 cm).

AFRICAN KNIFE FISH (*XENOMYSTUS NIGRI*)

This species ranges widely from the Nile River to West Africa. It is small for a knife fish, not growing more than 20-30cm. It is easily identified by its lack of a dorsal fin, and its conspicuous nasal openings. It has been a favorite of aquarists for a long time, but recently it is no longer all that common. It is a peaceful fish that can be kept with a number of other individuals of its own species. It prefers a somewhat higher water temperature.

Left: The African Knife Fish, *Xenomystus nigri*. **Below:** A Spotted African Featherfin.

AFRICAN FEATHERFIN (*PAPYROCRANUS AFER*)

This knife fish is easily mistaken for an arowana and it is sometimes called the Arowana Knife Fish. Its usual coloring is bright yellow spots sprinkled on a brown background, but some individuals may have a wild dappled pattern of spots and stripes. It is aggressive toward any fish that resembles it, not only its own species. It should be fed bloodworms, krill, and small live fishes. It has a strong constitution and is easy to raise successfully.

The African Featherfin is found in the Niger River, among other places, and grows to 80cm in its natural habitat. A related species, *P. congoensis* Roberts, 1991, was recently discovered, so now there are two species of *Papyrocranus*. Some differences are: *P. afer* has 10 or 11 gill rakers on the lower limb of the first gill arch while *P. congoensis* has 7 or 8; *P. afer* has 121-141 anal fin rays, while *P. congoensis* has 104-118; *P. afer* has more vertebrae, too, which is evidenced by its greater length from the dorsal fin to the rear tip of the body.

Many *Papyrocranus afer* are exported for aquarium use, but since many more fishes in general are now taken from the Zaire River, it is likely that some of the fish advertised as "solid *P. afer*" are in fact *P. congoensis*. *P. congoensis* reaches a length of 60cm.

Above: A Dappled African Featherfin. **Below:** A Solid or Patternless African Featherfin.

32

THE BASICS OF RAISING TROPICAL FISHES

FILTERS:

Filters do more than just physically remove impurities from the water; they also break down fish wastes and other noxious materials into less harmful or harmless substances. The use of a filter does not make changing water unnecessary. Rather, it is one essential part of the whole water purification process that provides a healthy environment for the fishes.

The undergravel filter, which is placed under the sand substrate, is most suitable for young fishes and small species. It is highly efficient but bothersome because cleaning the filter material, the sand, is tantamount to cleaning the whole tank. It is also no good for fishes that tend to dig in the substrate.

Good wet/dry filters are fitted to the tank size, and are designed such that the water stays in it long enough to maintain good contact with the filter media. These can also be hand made from sheets of chlorinated vinyl or acrylic.

Exterior power filters are very quiet and compact. They need only two tubes going into the tank, leaving lots of room for decorations. They come in a variety of types and sizes.

Sponge filters are best when keeping eggs or developing young. The diatom filter is convenient, especially when it comes to cleaning the aquarium.

FILTER MATERIAL:

The material inside the filter container is what actually filters the water. On the surface of the gravel, the usual material, are millions of microorganisms that do important chemical work. They convert harmful ammonia and nitrites into safer nitrates. Therefore, the larger the surface area of the material, the more these nitrobacteria can thrive. Nowadays, many excellent artificial filter materials are available. When they get dirty, all materials need to be cleaned, but this must be done without destroying all of the microorganisms. Cleaning only one section of the filter at a time is recommended, as this leaves a nucleus of material from which the biological filter bacteria can build up again.

WATER CHEMISTRY

pH and Hardness:

A pH of 7 is neutral, anything less is acidic, and anything more is alkaline. A change of pH of 1 point expresses a tenfold difference in the pH level. For example, if the pH drops from 6.8 to 4.8, then the water has become 100 times more acidic (ten times ten). Every fish is most comfortable at a certain pH level, but there is always a certain amount of flexibility.

Tap water is generally around the neutral level (this can be easily checked), and this is fine for most primitive fishes. The pH level is affected by the type of sand and the filter material. If neutral to slightly acidic water is desired, large granule sand is best. If slight alkalinity is the goal, then small granule or river sand should be used. Oyster shells and coral will effectively raise the pH (toward the alkaline side), and putting some peat moss in the filter box will safely lower the pH (toward the acid side).

The pH level drops as the water gets old and needs to be changed. A pH-meter or kit is all that is needed to determine when to change the water and is highly recommended. Of course, the chlorine must initially be removed from the tap water.

The value of the water's hardness expresses the amount of calcium and magnesium ions it contains. Most fishes prefer soft water. Fine sand will increase the water's hardness.

FOODS AND FEEDING:

Bloodworms are chironomid larvae which, when they mature, will not produce biting or stinging insects. They should be stored by wrapping them in wet newspaper, putting this in a plastic bag, and keeping them in

Accessories Necessary for Keeping Aquarium Fishes

Reverse Osmosis water purification system especially designed for the aquarium enthusiast, is one of many quality water treatment products manufactured at Aquathin Corporation of Pompano Beach, Florida. Photo courtesy of Aquathin.

Clear Flow Undergravel Filter courtesy of Hagen.

Supreme Ovation Filter courtesy of E.G. Danner Mfg.

Wet/dry Filtration System courtesy of Hagen.

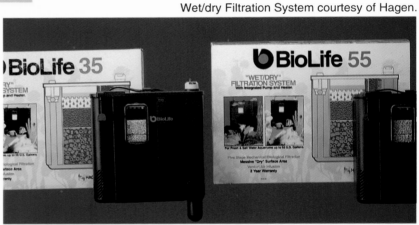

Power Filter courtesy of E.G. Danner Mfg.

Air Pumps courtesy of Hagen

Biospheres courtesy of Hagen.

Poly-Filter Wool courtesy of Hagen.

Ultragrade Carbon courtesy of Hagen.

Automatic Water Changer courtesy of
Aquarium Products.

Water Conditioner, Aquatic
Culture Treatment courtesy of
Mardel Laboratories.

a refrigerator. Tubificid worms (Itomimizu) should be kept in a cool place and the water changed at least twice a day. Some live bait that can also be used as food is also sold refrigerated. A number of different processed foods are sold which are vitamin-enriched and often contain a considerable variety of vegetable matter. The aquarist's motto should be "Don't overfeed."

PARASITES:

Argulus and *Lernaea* are both parasitic crustaceans that are able to invade the aquarium when mixed in with live foods or aquatic plants. If they multiply and become pests, the usual tactic for their destruction is to dissolve 3-5g of potassium permanganate per 10 liters of water, but less should be used when the aquarium contains primitive fishes.

Water Conditioner, Ultra Shield
Advanced Formula with
Seabond courtesy Mardel
Laboratories.

RAISING AROWANAS

by Hiroshi Maeda

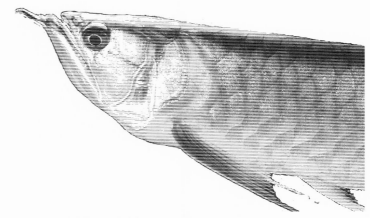

Silver Arowana, *Osteoglossum bicirrhosum*.

THE SILVER AROWANA (*OSTEOGLOSSUM BICIRRHOSUM*)

Now I would like to describe the basics of raising the Silver Arowana. The few differences that there are between raising this and the other arowanas will be pointed out afterward.

The Aquarium, Food and Feeding Methods, and General Care

When most Silver Arowanas (*Osteoglossum bicirrhosum*) are imported (to Japan), they are 4-5cm long juveniles still carrying a yolk sac. Young at this stage do not require any outside food source, and they are more adaptable to different water conditions than are their parents. However, they are sensitive to increases in nitrite levels, so care must be exercised in that respect. They like well-aged, neutral to slightly acidic water. When they have absorbed the yolk sac, they will seek out food on their own, but they are awkward at that age and have difficulty catching prey, so the tank should be small enough to permit easy feeding. As a general rule, a 10cm specimen should be raised in a 45cm tank, a 20cm specimen in a 60cm tank, a 40cm specimen in a 90cm tank, and, finally, a 120-180cm tank is needed for a fully mature Silver Arowana. When two or three individuals are kept in the same aquarium, the weakest will be harassed. This isn't a problem when there are more of them, probably because the larger population prevents them from staking out territories.

In the wild, the Silver Arowana begins feeding on animal plankton, small crustaceans, and insects that fall into the water. In an aquarium, once the yolk sac has disappeared, it can be fed well-cleaned live bloodworms by scattering them on the water's surface. Young Redfin make a handy meal for arowanas from a young age, but if only these are fed to the young fish, they may become spoiled and refuse to eat anything but the live fishes. The arowana will even eat *chikuwa* (fish sausage) if it is hungry, so its gastronomic adventurousness should be taken advantage of, especially considering the fact that a well-balanced diet means variety. From bloodworms move onto processed food, then try krill with the hard heads removed, as long as they are cut into bite-sized pieces that the arowana can handle.

For the mature arowana, all the foods mentioned thus far, plus slices of fish, *kamaboko* (boiled fish paste), and *chikuwa* are good. Overfeeding will result in floating leftovers, which are extremely bad for the water quality, so anything left uneaten should be removed as soon as possible and the amount of food reduced next time. Fish flesh is especially bad because it secretes oil that will float on the surface and overburden the easily-polluted filter.

A young Silver Arowana with its large yolk sac (6 cm).

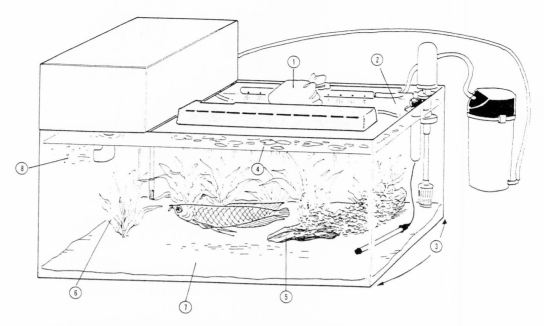

1) A sandbag weight. 2) Lid. 3) The tank should have enough width. 4) Floating plants. 5) Driftwood and stones with attached plants. 6) Amazon Swordplant. 7) Lay down a thin layer of sand. 8) The filter outlet tube should face the aquarium glass to keep the water calm.

A diet consisting of only fatty foods is as bad as one would think, and a diet of only goldfish and pond smelt is not very good either. An occasional dragonfly or other insect, a crayfish, killifishes, or other live fishes are good. But avoid feeding it cockroaches, since they probably contain a hefty amount of insecticide. Processed food is excellent for being nutritionally balanced. In short, balance through variety is the key to good feeding.

Water temperature is a factor but, generally, if the arowana grows 20-30cm in three to five months, it is developing well and needs a bigger tank. Some people try to slow the fish's growth by decreasing the amount or nutritional quality of the food, but this will probably lead to health problems later on, such as curvature of the spine. Once the fish has matured, though, one or two days a week should be made fasting days with no feeding at all. This will keep the fish's body fat down and increase its life span.

An arowana requires more surface area than depth, so the tank should be at least 2.5-3 times longer and 1.5-2 times wider than its body length. Tanks that are only 30cm wide and 60cm long are often sold but this is too cramped for the arowana to turn in and will eventually lead to a misshapen body. As it matures the arowana should be transferred quickly to a sufficiently large tank. When having a tank made-to-order, the length and width should be made roughly equal. Arowanas do not require much height or water depth if one is to be kept alone, but those aquarists who want to include other species, like catfishes, need more depth.

When transferring young fish, a net can be used, but, if possible, a plastic box or a strong, transparent plastic bag should be quietly slipped into the tank, and the fish caught and transferred along with the water. This method will prevent injury to the fish.

Filters and Water Replacement

Two methods of filtering should be used simultaneously in order to prevent sudden changes in water quality. If something should go haywire with one of the filters, the other will act as a backup. The protein and fat from the arowana's meat diet can quickly ruin the water quality. Even if it is kept in a large enough tank, a large fish cannot be kept without a correspondingly large filter.

The filter methods ultimately do

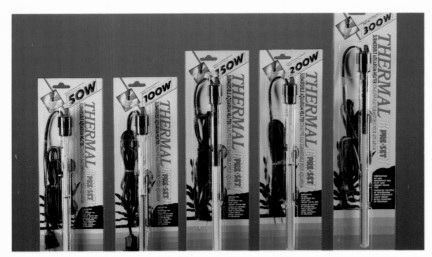

Thermal Compact Submersible Heater courtesy of Hagen.

Plantastics courtesy of Tetra/Second nature.

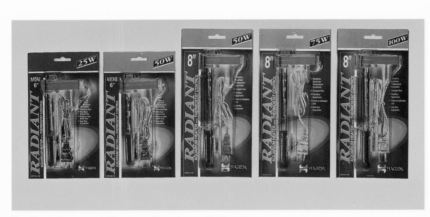

Radiant Compact Heaters Courtesy of Hagen.

Rydyt 1 courtesy of Python Products, Inc.

Tropical Fish First-Aid Center courtesy Aquarium Pharmaceuticals.

Digital Thermometer courtesy of Hagen.

pH Block Tablets courtesy of Fritz Chemical Company.

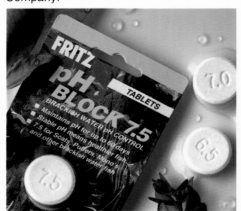

pH & Ammonia Test Kit courtesy of Fritz Chemical Company

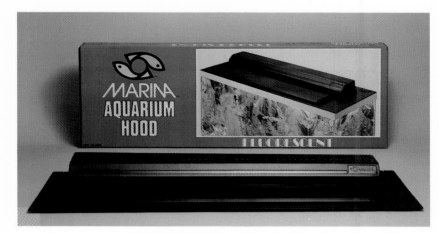

Aquarium Hood courtesy of Hagen.

Glass Cleaner photo courtesy of Phython Products, Inc.

Flake Food courtesy of Tetra/Second nature.

Lights courtesy of Energy Savers.

Algae Mit courtesy of Python Products, Inc.

Aquarium Planter Pads, Kit and Srips by Aquarium Pharmaceuticals.

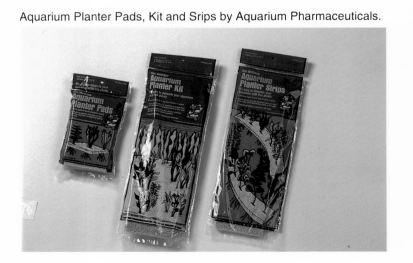

not matter. Arowanas do not dig in the sand, so a subsand filter is fine for a tank up to 60cm. However, if the subsand filter is overworked it can easily clog, which will mean having to empty the tank in order to clean it. Therefore, another filter should be used to remove the larger impurities from the water. If the subsand filter is used in conjunction with an exterior power filter or wet/dry filter, there should be no problem. These are much easier to clean, and the fishes (not to mention the aquarist) are spared the stress of their home being drained.

The water should be as still as possible, like the water of the arowana's natural habitat. Pumps that stir up the water will not be appreciated.

The water should be neutral to slightly acidic, but it is not necessary to worry much over this. As long as the nitrite concentration is around zero, the water is good. Of course, sudden changes are always dangerous, so only a third to a fourth of the tank's total volume of water should be replaced at one time. Again, it depends on the tank size and number of fish, but as a rule a fourth of the water should be changed at least once, preferably twice, a week. If the water quality calls for more changing, increase the frequency of changes rather than the amount.

Tank Layout:

Some say that it is easier to tell how dirty the water is if there is no substrate; in such an aquarium the bottom would have to be non-reflective. Arowanas get spooked by lights and shadows on the water surface and can leap right out of the tank, so a lid is necessary.

The arowana generally stays near the surface, so if the requirements of tank dimensions and filters discussed above are met the aquarium can be fully decorated. Some floating plants are fine, but long-stemmed plants that require a lot of maintenance should be rejected in favor of *Anubias* or Amazon Swordplants and rocks with Willow Moss or *Microsorium* growing on them. *Vallisneria* planted along the edges will soften the shock of any collisions with the tank walls.

Tankmates:

The Silver Arowana is the easiest of the arowanas to raise with other

Arowanas can be kept with large characoids. This is a red *Colossoma*.

fishes. It can cohabit with large characins, barbs, gars, *Polypterus*, and even cichlids, if there is a choice of species. Of course, any fish that can fit into the arowana's mouth or that can injure the arowana are out of the question. Other species of arowana are possible tankmates, but being living animals they have individual temperaments and need to be closely observed for a while after they are put together. Any injured specimen should be immediately moved to a treatment tank to recuperate. The Black Arowana (*O. ferreirai*) is jumpier than its silver cousin and should be watched more closely when they are cohabiting.

A Silver Arowana carrying eggs in its mouth. Photo furnished by Hiroshi Umizu.

Propagation:

The Silver Arowana is relatively easy to breed. It is a mouthbrooder that spawns and raises its young in pairs like cichlids. Breeders should be at least three or four years old, and a pair is sure to be formed out of a group raised together. Mated pairs give themselves away by swimming alongside each other much of the time.

When spawning, the pair swims around and around in circles, then the female lays her orange eggs, which are 8-12mm in diameter, and

the male fertilizes them. The number of eggs, only 100-300, is extremely small compared to other fishes. The newly hatched young stay in their parent's mouth for 40 days before coming out, at which time they are already about 3.5cm long.

A breeding tank should be at least 180 X 45 X 45cm. Depending on the geographic area that they come from, some breeders could be kept in an outdoor pond during the summer.

AUSTRALIAN AROWANAS

Cautions Regarding Raising the Two Australian Species of Arowanas

The two species of Australian arowanas, *Scleropages leichardti* (Spotted Barramundi) and *S. jardinii* (Northern Barramundi), can be raised in almost the identical fashion as the Silver Arowana. These species are generally called barramundi, except in Australia, where this name refers to *Lates calcarifer*. The arowanas are called Saratoga there. They are generally sold (imported) when young, and the care at this stage is like that of the Silver Arowana. They are good eaters and grow quickly. They are also strong swimmers, and the aquarium lid must have no gaps that they could leap through. Both young and old patrol their territory looking for fights, so they basically should be kept alone, or with another, completely different kind of fish. If the conditions are right, skilled aquarists are able to raise them with other arowanas. The Spotted

A young Spotted Barramundi chasing a killifish.

Barramundi is more sensitive to water quality than the Northern Barramundi. Compared to the arowanas of the genus *Osteoglossum*, they have less physical flexibility and need to be kept in a larger tank.

BREEDING SPOTTED BARRAMUNDI

Spotted Barramundis are reported to have been bred in ponds in their native region. Their natural habitat is limited, so pairs were introduced to ponds of 20 X 30 X 0.9-1.7m dimensions in October, 1975, and the presence of young was confirmed in January, 1977. The pond volume was approximately 540m^3, with a pH level ranging from 7.2 to 9.0, though lime wood chips were put in at first to maintain it between 7.0 and 8.0.

It is said that the male participates in sexual activity at least twice in a season, looking for a new, fertile female within several weeks of his first sexual encounter. The spawning season is in September and October when the water temperature is 22.5-23°C. Pond specimens spawn during the day while river specimens spawn at night. In the days before spawning, the pair spends a lot of time together swimming near the surface. The observed courtship behavior of the male involves swimming directly behind the female, repeatedly nodding his head and gently prodding her.

A female that is carrying eggs and young in her mouth is identifiable by her white jaws. The Spotted Barramundi tirelessly patrols its territory and fights often, but an egg-carrying female spends more time near the surface and will not fight non-egg-bearing females. Sometimes she will fight another mother, though, if she happens to encounter one. At water temperatures between 23 and 30°C, the eggs hatch after 10-14 days, then the 10-15mm young live in the mother's mouth for 5-6 weeks until they are spit out, having grown to 35-40mm. At this size they are on their own, although there is a transition period of three days during which the young enter and leave the mother's mouth. She watches the surroundings as they swim around her, some even straying to the edge of the pond. At the first sign of danger, she gives a signal and they all rush back into her mouth. After three days each youngster finds its own territory near the edge of the pond, but there are too many for any clearly marked boundaries.

These newly independent young are threatened by birds and bigger fishes. In this report, when the young continued to live with the parents after leaving the mother's mouth, twenty survived; but when the parents were taken away, forty young survived.

In 1969, Lake reported that this species could live in water at 40°C, but within its natural range, when the surface temperature reaches 31°C, it begins to swim at a greater depth. For raising, 25-27°C is a good range. In these reports the fish had plenty of space for territories. If this condition is met, breeding should be more than possible.

THE ASIAN AROWANA

Like the Australian Arowana above, the Asian Arowana is included in the genus *Scleropages (S. formosus)*. These are all more primitive than the species of the genus *Osteoglossum*, but the Australian and Asian Arowanas do exhibit some differences.

The Asian Arowana was first imported into Japan around 1970, but it was over-harvested as a "good luck" fish, and the population dramatically declined. There is little documentation or data on it, but it seems to resemble the Australian species in reproductive behavior. It is known that its survival rate up to one year is very good, but it must be a fully mature three– to five-year-old before it can reproduce. Attempts to speed up its maturation by feeding it highly enriched foods are likely to result in the specimen being unable to lay mature eggs because of internal fatty deposits. A rule to remember is: an 80% full stomach leads to a long life.

Fortunately, it has been successfully bred recently in Japan. However, the paltry number of young it bears, 30-80 eggs and 20-30 young, make the Silver Arowana look like the "old woman who lived in a shoe." The time periods of mouth incubation and protection are roughly the same as its Australian cousins, but it is slow to fully mature, and the reproductive rate per capita is low, perhaps due to the difficulty of providing a highly nutritional diet. Its

A cleared-and-stained specimen of *Scleropages formosus* showing the bony and cartilaginous structures. Photo by Dr. Guido Dingerkus.

A magnificent specimen of the Asian Arowana (*Scleropages formosus*) showing lots of red-orange coloration. Photo by K. L. Chew, Gan Fish Farms.

One of the Australian arowanas, *Scleropages jardinii*. Photo by M. P. & C. Piednoir.

A more subtly colored Asian Arowana. Photo by Dr. Herbert R. Axelrod.

A young Black Arowana that has already used up the nutrition of its yolk sac. If more external food sources were available it probably would still have some yolk left. Photo by Dr. Herbert R. Axelrod.

decline is a result of human influence and hopefully will be curbed with the protected status awarded it at the CITES Convention.

THE ASIAN AROWANA AND CITES

The Asian Arowana cannot be discussed without mentioning the CITES Convention. Widely known as the Washington Convention, the official name is the Convention on International Trade in Endangered Species of Wild Fauna and Flora, acronym CITES. First I will outline briefly the background of this convention.

In 1963, at the 8th International Union for the Conservation of Nature (IUCN), it was agreed that treaties regulating international trade in wild plants and animals should be made. After that, many drafts of a treaty were written up but none ever made it to the discussion table. In June, 1972, in Stockholm at the UN Human Environment Council meeting, it was recommended that "a meeting of appropriate governments or government agencies with full powers be called at the earliest opportunity in order to draw up and adopt a treaty regarding the import, export, and transportation of wild flora and fauna," which led directly to a joint proposal by Kenya and the U.S. based on the IUCN proposals to hold such a convention in Washington in 1973. Seventy-six trading nations and observers, including FAO, UNESCO, IUCN, and ICPB, attended. The result was that 72 countries signed a long and complicated pact that went into effect July 1, 1975.

Japan also signed the convention but the Diet failed to ratify it, causing considerable international criticism. It was finally ratified in May of 1980, and went into effect on November 4th of the same year. Now, every two years around the world renewal meetings are held in which the treaty is interpreted, addenda are distributed, and investigations of compliance are made.

On Dec. 1, 1987, a law enacting restrictions against trade in endangered species was proclaimed in Japan. This law was made to regulate domestic trade, because the borders were too difficult to monitor and CITES was ineffective against plants and animals and their products that had entered the

43

Asian Arowana.

country before ratification. This new law was created in order to comply with the spirit of CITES.

CITES is intended to prevent excessive international trade in specific endangered species; it recognizes the positiveness of moderate consumption, and seeks to promote balanced use. Humans have always relied on the products of nature to live, and it is far better to be able to continue making limited use of nature than to be forced to do entirely without.

Extinct species cannot ever return. Consider species that have become extinct recently. Population drops in the wild mean that there are fewer chances for the males and females to mate. In the broad seas and rivers members of the same species encounter each other less and less. There is less opportunity for selectivity in mating, leading to more interbreeding, more deformities, and more sickliness, a vicious cycle propelling a more rapid plunge into the void of extinction.

While there are species heading down this road right now, there are also species whose populations are being replenished with our help. It is the responsibility of everyone to aid somehow in the protection of these species. Since people take the surplus and the interest, they had better protect the principle.

The Asian Arowana was listed in the first appendix to the original convention as a highest class protected fish, but in 1989, at the Rosanne Seventh Review Congress, it was agreed to restrict the exportation of bred specimens from Indonesia. The number of specimens exported was 1250 in 1990, 1500 in 1991 and 2500 in 1992. That is the number exported to the rest of the world, not Japan's allotment.

This allowance continues to increase, with 3000 in 1993 and 4000 in 1994. They are all bred at a single fish farm, so wild specimens are not part of these exports. The size limit placed on exports is 15cm. Asian Arowanas can be imported under these restrictions for ornamental use, but we hope that aquarists will try to breed them as well. The recent successful breeding in Japan indicates that amateur aquarists can spawn them, too. When deciding whether or not to purchase one, please consider realistically if the proper conditions can be provided. Consider whether it will be satisfied with the conditions provided and live long enough to reproduce.

In March, 1992, the 8th Review Congress was held in Kyoto, and debates about ivory and tuna filled the newspapers. It was also an opportunity to rethink the fundamental tenets of the agreement. People are starting to realize just how complex the relationship between human management and conservation of nature is. What we need is a lot more careful thought and action.

PUBLIC AQUARIUMS

Since the purpose of the public aquarium is to display a large amount of aquatic life, the study of it may not always yield useful information for the average aquarist. With that said, in the Toribane Aquarium Silver Arowanas are kept with large fishes such as the Pirarucu (*Arapaima*), the Red-tailed Catfish (*Phractocephalus*), and the Jau (*Paulicea*). The tank is a large one, 12 X 5 X 3m. The area of the filter box is 30m², and it takes about 1.5 hours for all of the tank's water to pass through the filter. The water is dechlorinated tap water, with a roughly neutral pH.

The mainly biological filter uses an open gravity-style casing that is divided into four sections. These are required for the "reverse flush" system which prevents clogging that can lead to sudden changes in water quality. The direction of the flow through the filter is reversed regularly, one section at a time, to shake loose hardening filter gravel. The bacteria is shaken loose as well, but since only one section is backwashed at a time, filter efficiency changes little overall, and the water clarity remains excellent. Even with a number of large fishes that eat a lot, this filter is all that is needed to keep the ammonia, nitrite, and nitrate concentrations near zero.

The water temperature and circulation pump are controlled through the central observation room, and an alarm sounds if the temperature changes beyond specified parameters or if a pump malfunctions. As a precaution, the staff manually check the temperature on their twice-a-day rounds. There is also a terrarium section of the aquarium which is built to mimic the tropical shore, complete with artificial plants, rain, wind, snow, fog, and even rainbows.

This may sound like a spacious living arrangement for the arowanas, but consider the rest of the boarders. Two-meter-long Pirarucu, 1.5m long Red-tailed Catfish, and large Jau swim around them. Being chased by the Pirarucu may not be all that enjoyable. It must be especially rough at night when the lights go out and the catfishes that have hung around the bottom all day ascend to the middle and upper parts of the tank, crowding the poor arowanas even more. At 70cm, it is the pipsqueak of the tank.

At the Toribane Aquarium, they feed them pieces of fish like saurel once a day and it is quite a sight. The large catfish all rise up to the surface to feed. Even outside the tank, the sounds of fishes colliding and splashing are loud. Since the feeding is done only once and the arowanas are bound to lose any fight over a tender morsel, the staff always throw some fish directly to them.

DISEASES OF AROWANAS

Bulging Eye Condition

This is a common condition among Silver, Black, and Asian Arowanas, in which the upper part of the eyeball protrudes. The eyes of the afflicted specimen will continuously look down, but the arowana is tough and will continue to eat heartily. There are a few possible causes for this symptom, the worst being an infection from an injury near the eye. If this is not treated in time, it will

The aquarium's arowana tank, which also contains Pirarucu.

Open style gravity filter used in the aquarium.

Feeding time at the aquarium.

worsen until the eyeball falls out. However, most bulging eyeballs have no observable cause, and the arowana can swim and live healthily with entirely uneven eyes. Sometimes the protrusion is caused by a fatty deposit, but this is hard to treat and should just be left alone. There is a specimen in the Toribane Aquarium with a bulging eye, but no other fish in the reserve tank has the same condition and the cause is still unknown.

Gill Curling

When the covering of the fish's gills curls back to expose them, this may be caused by either a high concentration of nitrates or a lack of swimming space. In any case, this is a danger signal that must be heeded. The specimen is not in immediate danger of dying, but treatment should not be put off. Change the water frequently, create a more relaxed environment for it, and give it high-quality food. In short, take especially good care of it, and it should recover.

Spinal Curvature

This is most commonly seen in Silver and Black Arowanas. The causes are most often malnutrition when the fish is young and injury, but since the problem usually starts when the specimen is young, they need to be carefully checked for it before a purchase is made. As was mentioned earlier, the two Australian species are not as flexible as other arowanas and have to be kept in a relatively larger tank, or they may develop this condition. Once it develops, it is difficult to treat and a full recovery is virtually impossible. But if a decent environment is provided, this will rarely lead to the fish's death.

Other Conditions

Most other disease conditions and parasitic infestations are caused by infiltration of the tank by pests from outside, so care should be taken to check the condition of the food fishes and plants and apply disinfectants to them when necessary. The arowana is sensitive to fish medicines, so an ounce of prevention is worth many pounds of cure. Use any medicine sparingly and in conjunction with stepped-up regular care (water

Details of the head of *Osteoglossum bicirrhosum.* Photo by M. P. & C. Piednoir.

An arowana with a curling gill cover. Photo by Hiroshi Maeda.

A young *Osteoglossum bicirrhosum.* The yolk sac is already gone. Photo by Dr. Herbert R. Axelrod.

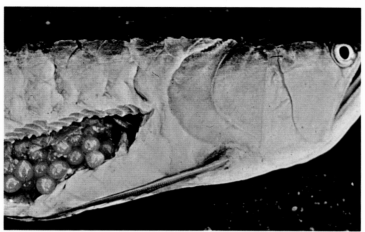

A female Silver Arowana dissected to show the large eggs (still not fully developed!). Photo by Dr. K. Lüling.

changes, etc).

Even if the nitrite concentration is low, if the arowana lives a long time in high concentrations of nitrates it will become prone to curling of the gill cover and eye infections. Water purity must be maintained by using a large filter box and frequently changing some of the water.

Finally, a leading cause of death is the fish leaping out of the tank, so a lid must be kept in place at all times.

A young Silver Arowana that still has the yolk sac. Photo by Dr. Herbert R. Axelrod.

Arowanas are also used for food in their native land. Here a fisherman proudly displays his catch. Photo by Dr. Herbert R. Axelrod.

RAISING OTHER PRIMITIVE FISHES: Pirarucu

by Shinya Mitani

TAXONOMY

The Pirarucu is classified in the order Osteoglossiformes, family Osteoglossidae, genus *Arapaima*, species *A. gigas.* It invariably appears at department-store exhibitions of exotic fishes with a commentary that says something like, "This fish has existed since 100 million years ago..." One is apt to be under the illusion that it swam between the legs of dinosaurs, but looking at the species level, this fish is a recent one. The question is at what level a fish is being called primitive, but if it is written that the Pirarucu has very primitive characteristics for an osteichthyan, we can pretty safely call it a primitive fish.

LOCAL NAMES

In English, this fish goes by the names Pirarucu, Arapaima, and Bony Tongue. The last name is the meaning of the family name, Osteoglossidae. Its tongue is extremely hard, and it is dried out and used as a file or grater by natives. Its local names are *pirarucu, arapaima*, and *paiche.* The first two names mean "red fish." In Brazil, the name varies with the size. Specimens up to a meter long are called *bodeco*, a meter-and-a-half and it's *bodecon*, and anything larger than that is called *pirarucu.*

RANGE/BEHAVIOR

The Pirarucu is distributed in the Amazon and Orinoco River basins and parts of Guyana. In the rainy season, it migrates from the rivers to the flood plains, and moves back to the rivers in the dry season. It spawns during the rainy season (either the first or the second half, it varies). With its fins it builds a saucer-shaped nest in the bottom sand and lays its eggs there. The number of eggs is very small, as little as 50 according to one report. The male and female guard the nest together after spawning. The eggs hatch after about ten days, and then the male nurses them with a milky fluid it secretes from its head. This

The Pirarucu, *Arapaima gigas.*

kind of care explains why the species can survive despite the small number of eggs.

Young are a blackish olive-green, but when they reach about 60cm they develop red speckles on the edges of their posterior scales and fins which contrast vividly with the dark background. From about 1.5m it looks like its name, "red fish."

The Pirarucu uses both gill respiration and aerial respiration. Once every ten or twenty minutes, it rises to the surface to take in air. Natives take this opportunity to harpoon them from behind. The hard scales would repel a frontal attack.

I have participated in many dissections of the Pirarucu. First, the scales are removed by making cuts with a scalpel and pulling the scales off with a pair of pliers, which was harder than I expected. Then the

Left: The exposed trunk of the Pirarucu. **Right:** The lung-like swim bladder.

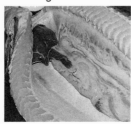 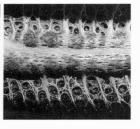

Dorsal view of a 9–to 10-foot Pirarucu. The red pattern is visible posteriorly. Photo by K. L. Chew, Gan Fish Farm.

A fisherman with four large Pirarucu in his canoe. As fishing pressure becomes more intense the average size of the fish caught will decrease. Photo by Harald Schultz.

scalpel can cut through the pink, tasty-looking flesh to the ribs, which are cut fairly easily. After removing the internal organs, a gray, intricate web-like organ can be seen. This wondrous organ is the swim bladder. Recently, it has been supposed that lung sacs disappeared and the swim bladder remained as a result of a reverse evolution. This means that the Pirarucu's ancestors had for some reason developed a secondary respiratory system that is still in evidence.

RAISING PIRARUCU

Tank and Filter:

The Pirarucu is not a fish for casual aquarists. The 10-15cm young that are sold in pet shops can be kept in a 90cm tank, but in a year they will grow to 60cm and require a 180cm tank. Then in three years they will exceed a meter in length, and in five years grow to be as long as two meters. A wealthy person can have a large enough tank made for it, but most people will have to tearfully say goodbye after hauling the huge fish to the local aquarium. They will appreciate your raising a fine fish, but it is best to avoid the trauma of moving the fish altogether by resisting any urge to buy one unless significant resources are at your disposal.

When it reaches 1.5m in length, it can be kept with other fishes as long as they are not small enough to be swallowed by the Pirarucu. At this size, other fishes are not a danger to it. However, 60-80cm specimens can be killed by the wrong tankmates. Once I mistakenly put a Pirarucu in with a snakehead (*Channa* sp.) and a Big-mouthed Catfish, and within an hour it had been ripped to shreds. The small size of the tank was partly to blame, but in general the Pirarucu should not be kept with aggressive fishes until it is fully grown.

In the Toribane Aquarium nine Pirarucus of 1.5-2m length are displayed in a 12 X 5 X 3m tank at 25°C with about 90 other well-known large fishes, such as the Silver Arowana, *Colossoma*, the Red-tailed Catfish, and the Jau. The weather of the jungle terrarium above the water's surface is changed every 15 minutes from wind to fog to squall. The tank is illuminated from 6 a.m.

49

to 6 p.m. We wanted to use direct sunlight to make a more natural environment, but the cost and the limitations of the building's structure made that unfeasible and we had to make do with full-spectrum fluorescent lights and halogen lamps. Sunlight, or a close imitation, brings out the natural colors of the fishes.

One disadvantage of direct sunlight is that it promotes algal growth. Also, gunk from floating food has to be scraped off the glass of the tank once a month, a task that takes a diver a few hours. If one enters the tank feet first, the Pirarucu assumes it is feeding time and rises up to nip at the diver's heels, so we jump in with a splash to prevent any unwanted advances. One time I was in the tank when the lights went out, and I saw the gold eyes of the Pirarucus gleaming in the pitch black around me. I was out of there in no time.

But I have diverged from the main point: the bigger the tank, the better for the Pirarucu, and the bigger the tank, the bigger the filter needed to purify it. At the aquarium, we use a 30m² gravity-style filter with a 180 metric ton capacity. The filter material is 0.6mm sand, but as long as physical and biological filtering can take place and water composition is not affected, any material should be fine. The Pirarucu prefers neutral to slightly acidic water, but it can gradually become accustomed to slightly alkaline water. It is an easy fish to raise in that it is not terribly sensitive to water conditions. Of course, as with any fish, sudden changes are usually deadly: many kept by amateurs die of pH shock. The aquarium water is continually replenished with desalinated water, but once a month a one-third water change is carried out to insure a pH of 7.0-7.2.

Sickness and Injury:

When a Pirarucu dies, the cause of death is often unknown. We have had fish around 60cm that were healthy and vigorous eaters until the evening before the morning when they were found curved like a bow, dead. One theory is that some bodily system was stressed by the fast growth that large fishes can attain in captivity with regular feedings. Another is that they are surprised by something and collide with the wall. Or perhaps their

Pirarucus are not for amateurs. They grow large very quickly and soon outgrow the largest tanks. They are best left to commercial aquariums. Photo by Dr. Herbert R. Axelrod.

The Pirarucu is skinned with a sharp knife. In many cases the scales are also saved and sold as souvenirs. Photo by Harald Schultz.

50

The fish is actually filleted. Here the fishermen are cutting the flesh away from the bones. Photo by Harald Schultz.

The fillets are laid out and dried in the sun. Photo by Harald Schultz.

swim bladder filled with water somehow, something akin to drowning, though I doubt this is the correct word in this situation. This "drowning" may be a cause of the deaths that occur during transport. Even at Toribane, if six 1-2 meter specimens are moved even a short distance, as many as four may die. The cause of this cannot be definitely ascertained.

While these mystery deaths are disturbing, the most unpleasant death is caused by the fish leaping out of the tank. Lids must be secure at all times and made of flexible, transparent, chlorinated vinyl. A strong net may do as well, but even at Toribane nets that appeared strong enough have been broken by the powerful leaps of Pirarucu.

Spinal curvature is common among specimens over 1.5m long, but it is impossible to tell if it will turn out to be fatal.

Food:

Pirarucu at the aquarium are rarely fed live fishes because we don't want them to eat them in front of the visitors, and because live fishes may contain parasites and are difficult to raise and keep. At Toribane, they are given saurel with calcium and vitamin tablets inside, but we don't know how much effect the pills have. These fish have never yet refused a meal, and it is important to feed them a variety from an early age. Goldfish, crucian carp, and *Moroco* are good menu choices. Two or three feedings a week should suffice, but how much they eat should be watched and the diet adjusted accordingly.

Conservation Efforts:

The size, good taste, and shelf life of the Pirarucu make it an important food fish in its native regions. There are restrictions on Pirarucu catches in Brazil: no Pirarucu under 1.5m can be fished, and there is a total ban on taking it from November to February, but these regulations are hard to enforce. Many immature fish are caught by hook and net fishing.

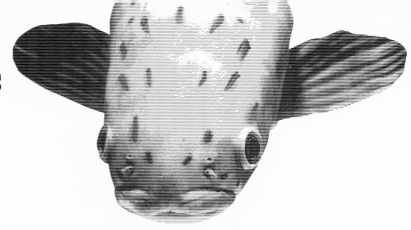

RAISING *HETEROTIS*

by Hiroshi Maeda

Heterotis niloticus is known as the Nile or African Arowana, but as a member of the family Osteoglossidae, subfamily Heterotidinae, it is actually a closer relative of the Pirarucu. Unlike the arowanas, *Heterotis* doesn't eat fishes but subsists mainly on plankton by filtering it out of mouthfuls of water with specialized gill rakers. Some specimens gulp mouthfuls of sand, filter out the organisms, and spit the sand back out.

The Nile Arowana is an easily tamed species. At Toribane it will take food from a person's hand. In captivity, its diet consists of bloodworms, tubificid worms, and often processed food. The water temperature is 24-28°C, and since *Heterotis niloticus* is not particularly sensitive to pH, around neutral is fine. Nitrate levels should be watched carefully, though. It tends to dig in the substrate, so bottom filters are not appropriate. Use exterior filters instead. Despite its generally peaceful appearance, it does fight with members of its own or another species, so new tankmates should be watched closely. However, completely unrelated species, such as catfishes, should present no problems. At Toribane Aquarium the Nile Arowanas are separated from each other by a transparent acrylic partition—and still they display threat behavior! At most they will grow to 90cm, so at least a 90-120cm tank is necessary.

Heterotis niloticus can really jump, so a firm lid and care when cleaning are important. I have had one suddenly leap out of the tank when I briefly removed the lid to clean. I quickly returned it to the tank, but it had fallen from a height of over a meter and injured itself pretty severely (both eyes bulged out). I thought it was done for, but it ate as usual and in two days was completely recovered. I had heard that African fishes were tough, but this was unbelievable. However, as a fish that needs to feed on plankton all day, it is easy to underfeed and it will grow thin quickly. Two feedings a day is the minimum.

The Nile Arowana rises to the

Above: The Nile Arowana, *Heterotis niloticus*.
Below: A Nile Arowana searching for food in the sand.

surface to inhale air like the Pirarucu. Since there is little documentation on its reproductive behavior I cannot verify this, but I hear that it lays several thousand eggs at a time, and both male and female care for the young.

1) Sandbag weight. **2)** Lid. **3)** Thin layer of sand.

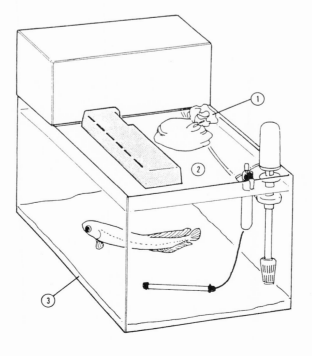

RAISING THE BUTTERFLY FISH (*PANTODON BUCHHOLZI*)

by Hiroshi Maeda

The Butterfly Fish stays near the surface watching for insects. Photo by Burkhard Kahl.

1) Plants should not interfere with the surface swimming area. **2)** Submerged power filter. **3)** Lid. **4)** A piece of driftwood with *Anubias* attached. **5)** A stone with *Anubias* attached.

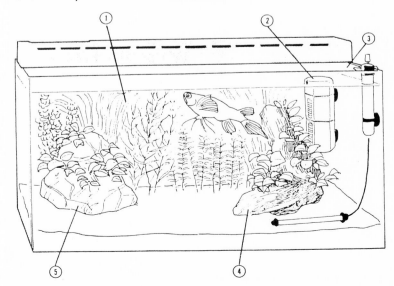

This is the only fish in the family Pantodontidae. It is small for a primitive fish, growing to about 13cm and requiring a 45-60cm tank for an individual and at least a 60cm tank for a pair. Individuals of the same species fight for territory, so they should be raised separately. As far as other species are concerned, Butterfly Fish will eat small fishes, and any fish that could injure the Butterfly Fish's long pelvic fin filaments (e.g., the Tiger Barb) is also undesirable. It is best to include some plants in the layout to help the fish remain calm, and it doesn't need depth as much as area since it tends to stay near the surface. It is said that it can leap a meter out of the water, so a lid is always necessary.

Any type of filtration method is fine as long as it is a quiet one. The Butterfly Fish is native to still waters, so if there is too much turbulence in the water it will not be able to detect insects on the surface. Peat should be used to maintain a slight acidity to the water, and the temperature should range between 25° and 29°C. It is basically nocturnal and eats surface insects and fishes, but in the aquarium it will eat bloodworms, tubificid worms, and shredded krill that are scattered on the surface. Killifishes are also good. It will ignore food that sinks to the bottom, so this must be siphoned out as soon as possible.

The female can be identified by her plumpness and the straightness of the edge of her anal fin. The male's anal fin is uneven. If a pair is being raised, there should be more hiding places near the surface, and more live food should be given. They spawn over a period of a few days while swimming in circles. The eggs, which are gray and float, hatch after three or four days depending on the water temperature. The young can only eat food that floats on the surface, making them a bit difficult to care for. Finely ground fish food and brine shrimp work well.

RAISING ABA ABA (*GYMNARCHUS NILOTICUS*)

by Fumitoshi Mori

TAXONOMY AND CHARACTERISTICS:

Inhabiting the Nile River and reaching lengths of 1.5 meters, the large *Gymnarchus niloticus* is classified in order Osteoglossiformes, suborder Mormyroidei, and family Gymnarchidae. It is a primitive fish with its own family, genus, and species (monotypic). Without pelvic, anal, or caudal fins, it swims by moving its long dorsal fin in a wavy, undulating motion. It can be easily distinguished from its close relatives of the family Mormyridae by its appearance and behavior.

Its head is large, and, unlike the mormyrids, it has a large mouth with a wide gape and powerful jaws. Since its eyes have degenerated, it is equipped with an organ system that can generate electricity for navigational purposes. A magnetic field is created around its body which enables it to detect organisms and obstacles that enter this field.

The Aba Aba was a very expensive fish when it was first imported into Japan, but nowadays 6-inch juveniles are regularly available from European exporters in London, Holland, and Germany. It seems that commercial breeding is well underway, and occasionally even highly prized albino specimens are imported.

CARE:

Mature Aba Aba are violent fish, but as with other species the young are rather delicate, so it is a good idea to begin raising them from an early age. If they are fed bloodworms, killifishes, or frozen foods, they can quickly grow to lengths of 15 centimeters or more. If several are kept together in a small tank they may bite each other's tails off, so it is best to raise them individually whenever possible.

Once they attain a length greater than 30cm their violent side begins to come out. If something gets near their mouth, they tend to bite first and ask questions later. Broken thermometers and thermostats are

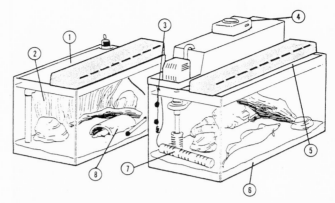

Aquarium setups for young (left) and mature (right) fish. **1)** Lid. **2)** Hardy plant varieties (ex. *Vallisneria*). **3)** Sensors (use 2 or more rubber coated sensors). **4)** Electric thermostat. **5)** Strong lid at least 5 mm thick. **6)** Coral sand mixed with large granule sand. **7)** Heater with a cover. **8)** Shelter using chlorinated vinyl tube section.

The Aba Aba has a long undulating dorsal fin. Photo by Klaus Paysan.

Albino Aba Abas are commonly on the market and always in demand. Photo by G. Meola.

not unheard of. I do not recommend keeping them with other large fishes, but it is often possible when the fishes are about the same size.

When preparing the layout of the tank, detailed aquascapes using plants should be avoided. Instead, it is best to use large rocks and driftwood to make a simple layout. It is good to use a top and a bottom filter together. The Aba Aba isn't picky about water conditions, but it helps to mix a little coral sand into the bottom sand to prevent the water from becoming too acidic.

PROPAGATION:

Wild *Gymnarchus niloticus* reach lengths of 1.5m or more, but this is rare in captivity, where 60-80cm lengths are more common. If the specimens have been imported from Europe, it is quite possible to breed them in the aquarium.

All osteoglossids display some kind of protective behavior toward their young. The arowana's females carry them in their mouths, and the male knife fish guard the eggs until they hatch. The male Aba Aba goes much farther, though, guarding the eggs and then the young all the way through to maturity.

There is no known method of distinguishing the males and females, and it is difficult to raise more than one in the same tank, so a successful breeding method is still a thing of the future. Thanks to advanced technology, raising the Aba Aba until maturity is easily accomplished, so now the creative energies in the field will turn to this challenge.

RAISING MORMYRIDS

by Fumitoshi Mori

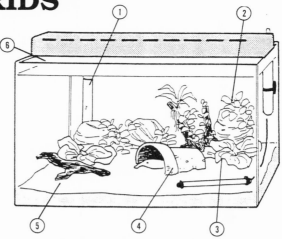

1) Either a bottom or top filter. 2) *Anubias*. 3) Tiger Lotus. 4) Half of a flower pot. 5) Small piece of driftwood. 6) Lid

TAXONOMY:

The popular mormyrids are a group of fishes, including the elephantnoses and the long-nosed elephantnoses, that are classified in the order Osteoglossiformes (the order that includes the arowanas and knife fishes), suborder Mormyroidei, and family Mormyridae. All mormyrids are distributed widely in tropical Africa in an area centered about the Nile. Sixteen genera and 190 species have been identified, and the variations in appearance among the family members are very great.

When we mention mormyrids, most people think of the typical Dolphin or Trumpet Mormyrus—fat bodies with protruding noses. The genera *Mormyrops*, *Mormyrus*, and *Miomyrus* all fit that description, and pet shops commonly sell species such as *Mormyrus kannume* and *Brienomyrus longirostris*. Another familiar genus is *Gnathonemus*, which is typified by the "elephant nose." But this genus is so hard to characterize, ichthyologists often disagree over the correct generic name for some of these species. According to Poll (1957), a new genus, *Campylomormyrus*, should be split off from the genus *Gnathonemus* based on the jaw and lip structure of the Double-trunk Elephantnose and the Longnose Elephantnose. Such divisions point out the variety of these mormyrids. The snouts of fishes of the genera *Polymyrus* and *Petrocephalus* do not protrude, and the snouts of the genera *Marcusenius* and *Stomatorhinus* protrude slightly. At present, the generic divisions are somewhat arbitrary, and the whole mormyrid family, which includes such popular species as *Ishichthis henry*, *Genyomyrus donny*, and *Hyperopisus bebe*, needs to be thoroughly reexamined.

CARE:

The best way to get to know the mormyrids is to raise one. Many well-known species, such as the Elephantnose, Dolphin Mormyrus, Double-trunk Elephantnose, and Donkey-faced Elephantnose, are

The "nose" is often just an extended lower lip as in this *Gnathonemus petersii*. Photo by M. P. & C. Piednoir.

A group of mormyrids will often stay in close proximity to one another as seen here. Photo of *Gnathonemus petersii* by Mark Smith.

56

Campylomormyrus rhynchophorus has an extended "nose" at a sharp downward angle. Photo by Edward C. Taylor.

regularly imported, while some other species are very hard to find, discovered mixed in with different species only once in a blue moon. It takes a long time to accumulate a really extensive collection of mormyrids.

Mormyrids can be raised mixed in a large tank, but alone in a small one is best. They are able to generate a weak electromagnetic field, and this leads to violent confrontations between fellow mormyrids.

Feeding has been a problem in the past. A typical diet of live foods, such as bloodworms and tubificid worms, would not suffice, and the mormyrid would grow thin even with regular feedings. Now it is best to use a variety of frozen foods with an eye toward nutritional balance.

A little coral mixed in with the sand substrate is recommended for preventing excessive acidity, and frequent water changes cannot be neglected.

Campylomormyrus sp. (possibly C. cassaicus) is very nicely patterned and therefore always in demand by aquarists. Photo by Edward C. Taylor.

RAISING KNIFE FISHES

by Fumitoshi Mori

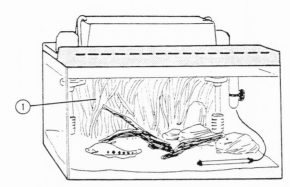

Plant a lot of plants (like *Vallisneria*).

TAXONOMY:

The knife fishes are a group of primitive fishes that are classified in the order Osteoglossiformes, suborder Notopteroidei, and family Notopteridae. They are distributed in the fresh waters of Africa and Southeast Asia. Until recently, the family Notopteridae was made up of three genera and five species, but the American ichthyologist T. R. Roberts published a revision of the family in 1991 and showed that it consisted of four genera and eight species.

The first genus known in the hobby was *Papyrocranus*, which is commonly known as the African Featherfin or Arowana Knife Fish. It has a thinner, more attractive body than the Southeast Asian knife fishes. The only commonly known species was *P. afer*, which ranges from the Niger River to western Sierra Leone, but according to new research, *P. congoensis*, which occurs in the Zaire River system and has no dappled pattern, is also included in this genus.

The genus *Xenomystus* is commonly known as the African Knife Fish and is identified by its lack of a dorsal fin. There is one species, *X. nigri*, which ranges all over tropical Africa from the Nile and Niger Rivers to the Congo (Zaire).

The Indian Knife Fish of Southeast Asia is dark brown and has a convex or only slightly concave craniodorsal profile. The single species known is *Notopterus notopterus*.

The other genus is *Chitala*, in which there are currently four species in all: the popular Clown or Spotted Knife Fish (*C. ornata*), which is characterized by several large ocellated spots on the body posteriorly, the Royal Knife Fish (*C. blanci*), which is characterized by having numerous oblique wavy lines posteriorly, the Southeast Asian Knife Fish (*C. lopis*), which is native to Indonesia, Malaysia, and Thailand, and usually displays a uniform coloration, and the Indian Knife Fish (*C. chitala*), which has blurred spotting posteriorly and is distributed in the Indus, Ganges, Brahmaputra, and Mahanadi River systems.

A very young *Papyrocranus afer* with dark spotting. Photo by Gene Wolfsheimer.

A larger African Featherfin with light spotting. Photo by Dr. Herbert R. Axelrod.

A magnificent specimen of the African Knife Fish. The light spots and dashes make this fish easily recognizable. Photo by M. P. & C. Piednoir.

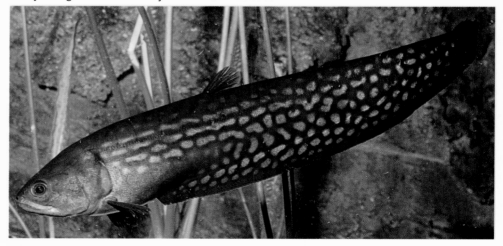

The African Knife Fish (*Xenomystus nigri*) is the only species in its genus. It lacks a dorsal fin. Photo by Klaus Paysan.

CARE:

The African Featherfin, the African Knife Fish, and three of the four species of *Chitala* are constantly imported (to Japan). They are large but have peaceful dispositions that make them a joy to raise. They like to hide in shadows and do not care for vigorous swimming much, so they do not require a very large tank. A 90cm tank will do for the average 60cm specimen.

Young 6-10cm specimens are easy to find, and they feed initially on bloodworms and krill, and then killifishes and small goldfish as they grow larger. We have successfully bred *Chitala ornata* in the aquarium, and any species should reproduce if they are put together in a 120cm tank and given time.

Probably the most common knife fish seen in aquaria is the Clown Knife Fish, *Chitala ornata*.

RAISING OTHER JURASSIC FISHES

RAISING THE BOWFIN (AMIA CALVA)

A. calva is the only known extant species of the family Amiidae and it is an extremely important fish for scientific study. Its common name comes from its long dorsal fin, which extends from just behind the head to the tail and undulates as it swims. The Bowfin grows to about 60cm, with the female usually larger than the male. The male is identified by a large black spot ringed with yellow or orange on its caudal fin base. In its native habitat, in April, the male builds a nest in plants and forces the female to lay eggs in it, an unusual reproductive behavior.

Bowfins should be kept in an at least 90cm tank, and since they become more and more aggressive as they grow older, they may eventually have to be kept alone. They will feed on small live fishes and shrimp, and processed food and krill are fine if they are slowly acclimated to it. A. calva is a hardy fish that will live a long time in the aquarium, but tends to be weak when young and often never make it to a healthy maturity.

Above: A young Bowfin. Note the prominent spot at the caudal base. **Below:** An adult Bowfin, *Amia calva*.

The Cuban Gar, *Atractosteus tristoechus*, is said to reach 2 meters in length.

RAISING THE GARS

Cuban Gar (*Atractosteus tristoechus*)

As the common name implies, this species is found in Cuba, where it is known as the "manfari." Once commonly seen all over Cuba and the surrounding islands, it is now limited to a few rivers on the mainland. Large specimens are said to reach two meters in length, but those in the aquariums of Japan are around 90cm. It has the widest snout of all the gars, and is greenish brown and lacks the patterns of the other species. There used to be specimens in the Ueno Aquarium and YomiuriLand in Tokyo but they are no longer on display. It is not imported as an ornamental fish and probably will not be in the near future due to its scarcity. Those that have been called "manfaris" in the past were probably Tropical Gars. This species is also known as *Lepisosteus (Atractosteus) tristoechus*. (Kuroiwa)

Alligator Gar (*Atractosteus spatula*)

This is the largest of the extant species, with a specimen 3m long and weighing 137kg recorded. It is also known as *Lepisosteus (Atractosteus) spatula*. It is found in large rivers, such as the Mississippi, and in rivers that run from western Florida to the Gulf of Mexico, as well as in some salt water areas along the Gulf. It preys on large fishes and reportedly sometimes catches waterfowl. While all gars are cylindrical with long heads, the Alligator Gar is noted for its exceptionally broad snout. It is a dark brown with an irregular pattern everywhere except the head and pectoral fins. The young have a white line that runs from the tip of the snout to the tail. The population is small, and many mysteries remain regarding its behavior.

As far as I know, it has only been imported into Japan once, in 1989, when some small (under 4cm) specimens arrived. All of these are now over one meter long. The

Top: A young Tropical Gar, *Atractosteus tropicus*. **Bottom:** An adult of the same species. Notice the pattern changes.

Alligator Gar grows very quickly in its first year, up to 80cm, even in an aquarium. It requires a very large tank or a pond and a great deal of food, so it is a fish best suited to a professional public aquarium. There are specimens known that have suffered from spinal curvature due to malnutrition in the growing period. (Kuroiwa)

Tropical Gar (*Atractosteus tropicus*):

This is the southernmost gar, with a distribution in the rain forests of Mexico and Central America

(Nicaragua and Costa Rica). It appears to be the smallest species of the genus, with growth stopping at 70cm in captivity, although it reportedly reaches 1.6m in the wild. Its snout is not as broad as that of the other species, and it resembles a fat Spotted Gar. Its color is close to that of the Longnose Gar and, except for the head, it is covered with black dapples centered around the lateral line. It is also known as *Lepisosteus (Atractosteus) tropicus*.

A few specimens were imported 7 or 8 years ago for display but they were extremely expensive. None have been imported since then as far as I know. Some specimens seem to have been mistaken for Alligator Gars or "manfari." Its care differs little from that of other gars, but it is thought to be more sensitive to temperature changes as it is from a tropical region. Its size makes it the best candidate for the private aquarium, and we can only hope more will be imported. (Kuroiwa)

Florida Spotted Gar (*Lepisosteus platyrhincus*)

This species is found from the Florida peninsula to southern Georgia in lowland swamps where Swamp Cedar flourishes and there are slow-moving rivers. It is very hard to distinguish from the Spotted Gar by casual observation, but it has a somewhat broader, shorter snout. It is also larger, growing to about 130cm.

Its range overlaps that of the Spotted Gar in Florida, but the Spotted Gar is not found in the eastern part of the state or on the peninsula, so imports from there may have been Florida Spotted Gar, impossible though it is to know now.

Shortnose Gar (*Lepisosteus platostomus*)

This species is found in the Mississippi River and its tributaries from Texas to Ohio to Montana. Its colors are subdued, and while it has no pattern like that of the Spotted Gar on its snout, there are large spots on its caudal, dorsal, and anal fins. The young have an indistinct pattern on the side that fades with age. There are individual differences in this pattern, but there are rarely variations among mature specimens, unlike among the Spotted Gars. The Shortnose Gar is on the slender side, with larger fins than the other gars. Specimens in this genus whose snouts are big and broad are often mistaken for the Cuban Gar. It grows to 80cm. It is imported in relatively large quantities, often mixed in with the Florida Spotted Gar, and it is frequently sold under the name of Alligator Gar or "manfari." It has also been handled under the name New Gar. There are no differences in care. (Kuroiwa)

A gold colored Florida Spotted Gar has shown up in the aquarium trade and has been well received. Photo by Dr. Harry Grier.

The normal colored *Lepisosteus platyrhinchus*. Photo courtesy of the Miami Seaquarium.

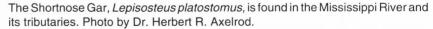

The Shortnose Gar, *Lepisosteus platostomus*, is found in the Mississippi River and its tributaries. Photo by Dr. Herbert R. Axelrod.

temperatures. All in all, this is an ideal fish for aquarists. (Kuroiwa)

Longnose Gar (*Lepisosteus osseus*)

This is the most wide-ranging of the gars, found as far north as Canada's Quebec Province. It is an old favorite that has been imported (to Japan) for a long time. It is known for its long, slender snout, and its body is a bright silver with black markings on the sides. It is a large species, growing as

Above, top: Shortnose Gar, *Lepisosteus platostomus*, with spotted fins. **Above, bottom:** A Shortnose Gar that lacks the spotting in the fins. **Right, top:** Young Florida Spotted Gar rising to the surface in a swamp. Photo by Shoichi Kazuishi. **Right, bottom:** A Florida Spotted Gar landed by a fisherman.

Spotted Gar (*Lepisosteus oculatus*)

Long the most popular species of gar, the Spotted Gar is distributed around the Mississippi River and the Gulf of Mexico from Mexico to western Florida. There are wide variations in body coloring, with the background ranging from nearly black to bright gold to silver, and the spots varying also from small to large. It can be acquired for a reasonable price in Japan, and it is the best gar for ornamental display since each specimen has its own unique pattern. Another advantage is its small size. In captivity, it will not grow longer than 60cm. Finally, since it originates in relatively northern waters, the Spotted Gar is highly adaptable to cooler water

Top: This Spotted Gar has uncommon markings. **Bottom, left:** A Spotted Gar with giraffe-like markings. **Right, center:** This is the most common pattern in Spotted Gars. **Bottom, right:** A very young Longnose Gar, *Lepisosteus osseus*. Photo by Braz Walker.

A young *Lepisosteus osseus* with its spotted pattern. Photo by Andreas Spreinat.

Lepisosteus platostomus in a photo tank. Photo by Dr. Herbert R. Axelrod.

An adult *Lepisosteus spatula*. Photo by Ken Lucas, Steinhart Aquarium.

The Spotted Gar, *Lepisosteus osseus*. Photo by Dr. Herbert R. Axelrod.

Above, top: A Longnose Gar stalking a sunfish. **Above, bottom:** After grabbing its prey between its long jaws, it will adjust its grip in order to swallow it head first.

A young Longnose Gar of about 6 cm length.

long as 180cm. The guidelines for raising the Longnose Gar are similar to those of the other gars except that special care has to be taken not to give it food that is too large for its narrow mouth. Since it is especially good-natured, it may be attacked by other fishes and its lower jaw can be broken, so it should not be kept with aggressive fishes. The Longnose Gar also needs extra tank room in which to maneuver its ample snout. Having braved the chilly rivers of the great frozen north, it is the most tolerant of cool water and would do well in an outdoor pond. (Kuroiwa)

RAISING BICHIRS

Speckled Bichir (*Polypterus retropinnis retropinnis*)

This is a small (25cm) species of *Polypterus* from Zaire that was imported (to Japan) in great numbers in 1981 but hasn't been seen at all since. It is usually yellow-brown, but black specimens also exist. Irregular speckles decorate its sides, sometimes in a crisscross pattern. It differs from the supposed subspecies *P. retropinnis lowei* in that *P. retropinnis retropinnis* has a flatter head and its coloring is more subdued. After it started to be imported, it became famous for turning white. Although some specimens actually did turn a ghostly white, we hear that others returned to their usual color after a week or so. It should present no special problems to aquarists, but crevices and filter openings should be checked out because *P. retropinnis* is thin enough to slip into or through a tight spot. It will feed on krill, bloodworms, and small fishes of appropriate size. (Yamazaki)

Rope Fish (*Erpetoichthys calabaricus*)

Native to Nigeria and Cameroon, this "stretched-out" *Polypterus* is the only species of its genus, being unique in its body shape and lack of pelvic fins. It is known as the Rope Fish or Reed Fish. There are 7-13 small, separate dorsal fins spaced slightly apart on its back, and its head resembles that of members of the genus *Polypterus* in its protruding upper jaw. In fact, it looks a bit like *P. weeksii*. Its back is a greenish brown turning to yellow on its belly. The only notable marking is a large black spot at the base of the pectoral fin. It grows

to a length of 40cm, but growth is extremely slow so a 45-60cm tank should suffice. It eats bloodworms, killifishes, and krill. Large specimens will also eat small goldfish bred specifically for food. Lastly, as one would expect by looking at its body, there is a danger of it slipping through cracks, filter tubes, and so on. (Yamazaki)

Poll's Bichir (*Polypterus polli*)

This is the most recently named

Above: The Rope Fish, *Erpetoichthys calabaricus*. **Below, top:** The Speckled Bichir, *Polypterus retropinnis retropinnis*. **Below, bottom:** Poll's Bichir, *Polypterus polli*.

species of the genus, the paper being published by Jean-Pierre Gosse of the

Belgian Royal Nature Research Center in 1988. It was originally described by Max Poll of the Belgian Royal Museum in 1954 as *P. palmas congicus*, but this was a junior homonym (the same name for different species) of *P. endlicheri congicus*, which was described as *P. congicus* by George Albert Boulenger of the British Museum in 1898. Since these two designations could not exist simultaneously, the name was replaced by Gosse, who designated it *P. polli* to honor the original describer.

The range of this 30cm fish is the middle and lower Zaire River. The spaces between its 5-7 distinct dorsal fins are very small, and it has a distinctive band on its body. It is peaceful but will be aggressive toward its own kind. Its needs are the same as described for the other species of *Polypterus*. It may be sold in shops under the designations *P.* sp. or *P. congicus*. (Igarashi)

Lowe's Bichir (*Polypterus retropinnis lowei*)

This is a medium-sized (40cm) species of *Polypterus* that is distributed in Liberia and southern Cameroon. Its brownish coloring is tinted with yellow or green, fine black spots cover its head, back, dorsal and caudal fins, and several indistinct yellow bands extend obliquely down from its back. It is the spitting image of *P. r. retropinnis*, but *P. r. lowei* has a larger head and a somewhat brighter body color. This is currently considered a subspecies of *P. retropinnis*, but the latest research

Above, top: Week's Bichir, *Polypterus weeksii*. **Above, below:** A green *Polypterus weeksii*. This individual is still quite young. **Below:** Lowe's Bichir, *Polypterus retropinnis lowei*.

suggests that this may be a synonym (two names for the same species) of *P. palmas*. Albinos used to be fairly common but they have disappeared lately. We have heard of no case of successful breeding in Japan, and would love to try our hand at it. (Yamazaki)

Week's Bichir (*Polypterus weeksii*)

Occurring in Zaire, there is a sharp difference in color between its back and underbelly, the back usually being a grayish or yellowish brown with 7-9 dark bands that may fork toward the bottom in some specimens. Like *P. palmas*, the green-headed specimens are especially prized for their beauty. The black markings on the caudal fin are also striking. *P. weeksii* is distinguished by its large, round head. The exterior gills of the young remain until they grow quite large; in fact, many still have them at 20cm. Growth is slow, ending at around 40cm in the aquarium with the exception of the occasional 60cm "heavyweight." Week's Bichir is a very mild-mannered fish so cohabitation with other fishes is generally no problem, but it may eat even fishes that seem much too big for it to handle. For example, we know of a 30cm specimen that ate a 15cm gar, so the bigger the tankmate, the safer it will be. It frequently swims along the surface so a heavy weight on the lid is a necessary precaution. (Yamazaki)

Armored Bichir (*Polypterus delhezi*)

Found in Zaire, *P. delhezi* has been imported into Japan for a long time and is very popular because of its extremely graceful swimming style. It is identified by its relatively small head, and the fact that its dorsal fins begin relatively far anteriorly. Its color is gray with yellow or green running through it, and there are 7-8 bands slanting down from its back. The thickness and positioning of these bands differ greatly between individual specimens. Many 10cm young have become available lately so the aquarist can pick out his or her favorite. It quickly doubles in size, then growth slows surprisingly fast, but it will still reach 40cm in a roomy tank (around 90cm) where it can swim freely. Its diet is the same as that of the other species, but as its head is small for its body, the food should be accordingly bite-sized. (Yamazaki)

Marbled Bichir (*Polypterus palmas*)

A small (30cm) species occurring in Zaire, Sierra Leone, and Liberia, *P. palmas* has a crisscross pattern on its brown back which becomes indistinct from the center of its body to its head. The head and pectoral fins have green on them, but the intensity and timing of the coloration depends on the individual specimen and the water composition in which it is raised. The latter can be manipulated by the aquarist until the best water for bringing out the colors is found. Black coloring generally appears in older specimens. The head is relatively small and the upper jaw protrudes. Individuals tend to get fat as they age, this being more noticeable in the females. The Marbled Bichir is a very solid fish, not at all timid, an excellent eater and highly adaptable to new surroundings, so along with *P. senegalus* it is an excellent fish for beginners. There are many reports of the successful spawning of this species as well. (Yamazaki)

Ornate Bichir (*Polypterus ornatipinnis*)

Native to Lake Tanganyika and the Zaire basin, *P. ornatipinnis* is the biggest of the protruding upper jaw type, easily exceeding 60cm if given enough living space. The striking black and yellow checkerboard pattern is its most notable characteristic, and specimens with large, clear yellow spots are extremely beautiful. Green coloring around the mouth is not uncommon. The black and yellow stripes on the pectoral fins are annual rings; like tree rings, they indicate the fish's age. Its body type is like that of *P. weeksii*, but more slender and with a flatter head. The Ornate Bichir is very popular and young of 5-10cm are easily obtained. The only caution for potential raisers is to remember that even cute little youngsters will one day be pretty big grown-up fish. (Yamazaki)

Above, top: The Armored Bichir, *Polypterus delhezi*. The banding is quite distinct in this individual. **Above, bottom**: A green form of the Armored Bichir. The color may be due to something in its diet.

Above, top: The Marbled Bichir, *Polypterus palmas*. **Above, bottom:** The Marbled Bichir from a different angle. The belly of many fishes is usually unpatterned.

Above: Adult Ornate Bichir with many "annular rings" on its fins.
Left: A young Ornate Bichir, *Polypterus ornatipinnis*, of about 9 cm.

Red Bichir (*Polypterus endlicheri endlicheri*)

This fish inhabits the waters of Nigeria, Lake Chad, and the White Nile, and grows to a length of 60cm or more both in the wild and in captivity. Imported young are generally gray or brown or reddish, but many gray ones suddenly develop gorgeous red coloration as they mature. It usually has 5-7 broad bands slanting down from its back which differ among individuals, with some running straight down, others dividing up into two or three bands, and in some rare cases, overlapping to make "X" patterns on its side. Black spots can be found on the head, underbelly, edge of the dorsal fins, and the caudal fin. On the pectorals are either spots or annual rings. The head is very flat, the lower jaw protrudes, and as it grows heavier the back starts to bow. Extremely popular for its powerful appearance, there are more than a few collectors who deal exclusively in this species. It was first imported (to Japan) in 1981. It will feed on small live fishes and shrimp as well as frozen shrimp and krill. (Yamazaki)

The Red Bichir, *Polypterus endlicheri*. As can be seen here, the overall impression one can easily receive from *P. endlicheri*—or from any of the less elongated bichirs, for that matter—is one of controlled power. The fish has the size and the musculature to be destructive, and exuberant movements such as tail-lashings and side-to-side shimmying performed in a confined space can have a tendency to do damage to in-tank equipment that is not properly secured.

Not generally regarded as overly pugnacious against fishes near its own size that are confined with it, *P. endlicheri* nevertheless includes occasional individuals that are very nasty to both other species and their own kind. This consideration, of course, is completely separate from the question of which fishes a bichir like *P. endlicheri* will eat; in general it will eat just about any other fish that it can cram into its maw.

Above, top: A Congo Bichir in a community tank with some *Datnioides*. **Above:** A young *Polypterus endlicheri congicus* that still has an external gill above its pectoral fins.

Congo Bichir (*Polypterus endlicheri congicus*)

This subspecies comes in three colors, gray, yellow, and brown, with 6-10 somewhat thin vertical bands extending down from the back and two or three stripes running from the rear of the gill flap to about the center of the body. Some specimens, usually the browner ones, have black spots on the head, pectorals, dorsal fins, and upper caudal fin. Its head is flat, but somewhat thick compared to *P. e. endlicheri*. Furthermore, while it grows fairly fat, it is not quite as heavy as some related species. It is known as the "kambare-mamba" in one native tongue (Swahili?) of Tanzania (it occurs in Lake Tanganyika). Kambare means catfish, and mamba means crocodile. In the wild it reportedly reaches a length of 97cm, and it grows very quickly in captivity, one specimen growing from 25 to 63cm in a single year. (Yamazaki)

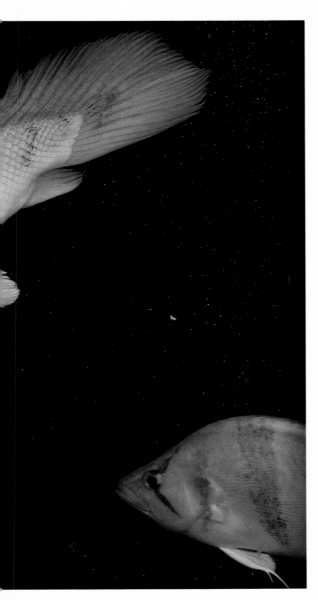

West African Bichir (*Polypterus bichir lapradei*)

This species ranges all over West Africa and generally reaches 50-60cm in length in captivity, although large specimens may push 80cm. There are three known extant subspecies of this patterned species, and this one at least is imported for display. The original species was described in 1869 by Franz Steindachner, a scientist who studied insects, amphibians, and fishes, but in 1941 this subspecies was created by the Belgian ichthyologist Max Poll, who passed away in 1991. I have previously used the "ii" ending (*lapradii*) for the subspecific name, but have changed the spelling to "ei" (*lapredei*) to be consistent with the original description. The literature gives its size as 74cm, but this is very large compared to the specimens we have kept. The lower jaw protrudes slightly, and it has 13-16 distinct dorsal fins, though one exception with 17 has been noted (in a similar case I, myself, have owned a *P. e. endlicheri* with 16 rather than the usual 12-14 dorsal fins). It is green in hue with stripes and bands that are especially attractive in the young. It is somewhat violent, especially toward its own kind, but a calm environment should serve to help it settle down. Its care is like that of other related species. (Igarashi)

Below: The West African Bichir, *Polypterus bichir lepradei.*

BREEDING *POLYPTERUS SENEGALUS*

By setting up the aquarium with the aquatic plants necessary for spawning, reproductive behavior was induced. This case history shows us that the reproductive behavior of *Polypterus* species is typical.

As spawning season approaches, the males act more and more aggressively toward each other.

The male's anal fin grows larger. He will use this fin to clasp the female during spawning.

The female's anal fin is much smaller and thinner.

A male pursuing a female. The chase might last for several hours to half a day.

Above, top: Now the pair poke their heads through a plant (*Bolbitis*) that will serve as their nest. They "prepare" it so that they can swim through the plant together. **Above:** With their heads and torsos poking out of the plant, they can spawn in the spawning "cave," that is, the plant. With every fin standing erect, the female deposits several eggs at a time.

CUVIER'S BICHIR (*POLYPTERUS SENEGALUS*)

This is a very wide-ranging species, found in Senegal, Gambia, Nigeria, Lake Chad, the White Nile, Lake Rudolf (L. Turkana), and the Katanga region of Zaire. According to some scientists there are three subspecies,

First row, left to right: A brand new egg. Most of the eggs were weakly adhesive and found in the aquarium gravel. A developing egg. Depending upon the water's condition, roughly half of the eggs suffered from fungus attacks. A newly hatched young. The resemblance to a tadpole is striking. **Second row, left to right:** A young fish that has nearly exhausted its yolk. It swims vigorously at this stage. With its exterior gill erect, this youngster has started to acquire the shape of an adult *Polypterus*. It feeds on *Artemia* and is about 15mm long. A youngster of about 20 mm length. The young should be separated into small containers in order to keep them from eating each other.

P. s. senegalus, P. s. meridionalis, and an as-yet-to-be-named subspecies discovered by Boulenger (1909) in the Nile system. In the wild it reaches 40cm, but 30cm is a more common length in captivity. It is a basic gray without special markings. Like *P. palmas*, it is a strong, adventurous fish that is recommended for beginners. The upper jaws of many imported specimens have been smashed en route, something to watch out for when shopping for one because it rarely heals properly. Since it is unpatterned, it is easy to see the ganoid scales, the distinct dorsal fins, and the spines of the fins. All in all, it is an excellent species for studying *Polypterus*. There are many reports of successful breeding. (Yamazaki)

An albino *Polypterus senegalus*.

Young Little Sturgeon, *Acipenser ruthenus.*

Young European Little Sturgeon, a hybrid, *A. ruthenus* X A. stellatus.

RAISING THE STURGEONS
Little Sturgeon (*Acipenser ruthenus*)

This sturgeon has been imported longer than any other. It is comparatively small, rarely reaching a meter in length. It ranges from the Caspian and Black Seas to northern Europe, and is more strictly fresh water than the other species.

European Little Sturgeon (*A. ruthenus* X *A. stellatus*)

This hybrid can be distinguished from a pure *A. ruthenus* by its longer snout, whiter belly, and the blunt ends of its scales.

Above, left: Young White Sturgeon, *Acipenser transmontanus.*
Above, right: Young Colored Sturgeon, *Acipenser sinensis.*

White Sturgeon (*Acipenser transmontanus*)

This sturgeon is found along the Pacific coast of North America in rivers that flow into the Pacific. It can reach 4m in length. Sturgeons are known for their longevity, and one individual of this species is said to have lived 82 years. It also takes a long time for them to mature, about 15-20 years.

Colored Sturgeon (*Acipenser sinensis*)

This species occurs in China and the Korean Peninsula, and specimens have even been caught off the Japanese coast. It was first imported via Hong Kong as an aquarium fish in 1991. It grows to about 1.2m in length.

Great Siberian Sturgeon (*Huso dauricus*)

This fish is widely known as the Kaluga, and is distributed in the Amur River and on the Chinese coast. The other species of this genus, *H. huso*, is known as the Beluga and is highly prized for its roe (caviar). Both grow to 4m in length. It hasn't been imported (to Japan) yet for aquarium display.

Adult *Huso dauricus.* Photo by Fumitoshi Mori.

Baikal Sturgeon (*Acipenser baeri*)
Found in Siberia and on Sakhalin Island, this sturgeon grows to 1.4m. It may be more suited for raising than the other sturgeons since it is a freshwater species, but it has never been imported for that purpose.

Top, left: A Baikal Sturgeon, *Acipenser baeri*. **Top, right:** The number of sturgeons in Lake Baikal has plunged so dramatically that fishing for them is completely banned.

Bestel (*A. ruthenus* X *H. huso*)
Sturgeon are bred for caviar, so hybrids are created in the hope of increasing roe output. The Bestel combines the tolerance of warm water and early maturity of *A. ruthenus* with the rapid growth of the Beluga.

Shovelnose Sturgeon (*Scaphirhyncus platorhyncus*)
There are three species in this genus, but only this one has been imported for aquarium display. It occurs in the Mississippi River basin, and is acclimated to warm water (18-28°C). It grows to 1.5m.

Above, left: The Bestel, a hybrid, *A. ruthenus* X *H. huso*. **Above**: Shovelnose Sturgeon, *Scaphirhynchus platorhynchus*.

Paddlefish (*Polyodon spathula*)

The unforgettable spatula-like snout of the Paddlefish takes up a full third of its about 2-meter-long body length. It occurs in the Mississippi River, swimming along with its mouth open and filtering plankton through its numerous gill rakens. There are two monotypic genera of paddlefishes, and both this and the Chinese species are in decline. *P. spathula* was listed in Appendix II of CITES.

Top, left: A young Paddlefish (15 cm). **Top, right:** An albino Paddlefish. **Above:** A Paddlefish about 70 cm long.

An extremely rare underwater photo of *Neoceratodus* in its natural habitat.

Above, left: A river inhabited by lungfish. There is a great deal of plant life and shrimp in this river. **Above, right:** A train station named for the extinct *Ceratodus*. The station is no longer in use.

A specimen of *Neoceratodus* that was captured (with permission) and released immediately afterward. Photo by Atsushi Sakurai.

RAISING LUNGFISHES
Queensland Lungfish (*Neoceratodus forsteri*)

Trade in this species is banned under Appendix I of CITES, and it is heavily protected in its native Australia. It has the most primitive anatomy of the lungfishes, with paddle-like pectoral and pelvic fins and very large, thick scales. The only extant species of its order, it is a direct descendant of the extinct Triassic lungfish *Ceratodus*. With lungs that are not highly developed, it depends on gill respiration more than lungfishes of the genus *Lepidosiren*. It doesn't hibernate, and grows to a meter in length.

Top: South American Lungfish, *Lepidosiren paradoxa*. **Bottom:** African Lungfish, *Protopterus annectens*.

African Lungfish (*Protopterus annectens*)

This species ranges from western to central and southeastern Africa, and reaches a length of 60-80cm. It was described by Richard Owen of the British Museum in 1839. Then *Protopterus annectens brieni* was described by Max Poll in 1961, so that now two subspecies are known. Those that are sold for aquarium use are usually *P. a. annectens*, of which 10cm young have recently become available for a decent price. They may have many markings, which may resemble fingerprints, or they may have no markings at all. There are a lot of individual differences in color as well. The African Lungfish grows quickly, and a mature specimen may still show traces of the exterior gill it used in its youth.

Protopterus annectens is a bit more high-strung than other species of the genus, and it reacts nervously to feedings or water changes. The strong teeth and jaws have to be watched closely at those times. *P. dolloi* has been successfully bred recently, but there is no definite information on the other species. In the wild, breeding is limited to the rainy season as in Gambia where within a month or two of awakening from the summer hibernation (August or September) spawning occurs in the swamps that are wet from rain and river overflow. (Igarashi)

South American Lungfish (*Lepidosiren paradoxa*)

This monotypic lungfish is distributed in the Amazon, Paraguayan, and Bolivian Rivers, and reaches one meter in length. When young, it has beautiful yellow spots on its black basal coloring, but these spots fade with age and mature specimens are almost entirely black. Its small, whiplike pelvic and pectoral fins are far apart. The long thin body resembles that of *Protopterus dolloi*.

During the rainy season, which runs from April to September, it feeds a lot, especially on shellfish, preparing for the dry season. When that arrives, *L. paradoxa* burrows into the mud to begin its summer hibernation. It differs from *Polypterus* in its hibernation behavior: It digs and enters its hole, then covers the opening, leaving small holes through which it can breathe.

When the rains return, it is the beginning of the breeding season. The male digs a nest in the muddy bottom and guards the eggs that the female lays there. At this time, the male develops 5-7 stringy protuberances on its pelvic fins. Their function is not clearly understood, but one theory is that they are secondary respiratory organs developed for the crucial time of egg protection. The eggs are 6.5-7mm in diameter, and the newly-hatched young have exterior gills that they usually lose by an age of six weeks. It has a peaceful disposition and can actually be raised in groups, making it an excellent candidate for aquarium breeding. It feeds on bloodworms as well as processed food. It prefers slightly acidic soft water. (Yamazaki)

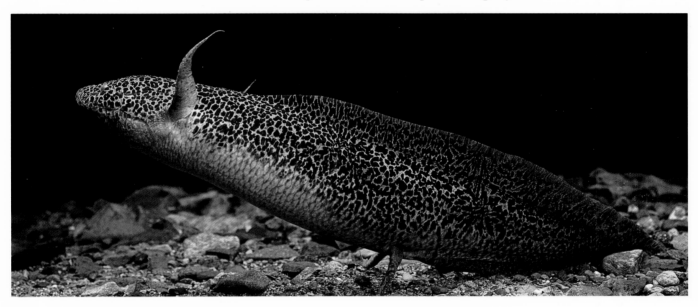

Above: Kamongo, *Protopterus amphibius*. **Left:** A young *Protopterus amphibius* (3.5cm).

Kamongo (*Protopterus amphibius*)

This is the smallest species of the genus, with a total length of 60cm. It is distributed in the Zambezi River and Lake Rudolf (Lake Turkana). Characteristics that make it easy to distinguish from other species include its round head, the anterior origin of its dorsal fin, and the broadness of its pectoral fins. The exterior gills are thought to remain throughout its whole life. The body is generally gray, but specimens with black spots on a red or yellow background are not uncommon. They are easy to raise, living on processed food as well as small live fishes and shrimp. The young do well with bloodworms, but it is sometimes fun to feed them just one shrimp. The young lungfish seems to think it is an intruder and it threatens the shrimp by opening its mouth wide and flexing its body. This shows the strength of the territorial instinct, so the ideal situation is to raise this species by itself. (Yamazaki)

A young *Protopterus aethiopicus* (23 cm).

A one-meter-long *Protopterus aethiopicus*.

Speckle-bellied Lungfish (*Protopterus aethiopicus*)

This species is distributed in Central and East Africa, primarily in Lakes Victoria and Tanganyika. Even in captivity it frequently exceeds a meter in length, and wild specimens two meters long are common. In fact, there is such a mounted specimen on display in the Nairobi Museum. Solid colored specimens are often mixed in with *P. annectens*, but *P. aethiopicus* can be identified by its dorsal fin, which originates farther posteriorly. The basic color is usually yellow or brown, though some milky white specimens exist. On this can be seen black or green spots, or a tortoise-shell pattern. Albinos are fairly common. This is a beautiful lungfish, and a big one, too, that lives a long time so that raising it requires proper long-term planning. Three subspecies, *P. ae. aethiopicus*, *P. ae. congicus*, and *P. ae. mesmaerkersi*, have been described. (Yamazaki)

An albino
*Protopterus
aethiopicus.*

Spotted African Lungfish (*Protopterus dolloi*)

This species of *Protopterus* is found in Zaire. Reaching a length of 80cm, it is the longest member of the genus. It closely resembles the South American genus *Lepidosiren*, except that *P. dolloi* can be easily identified by its longer pectoral and pelvic fins. *P. dolloi* also resembles the Electric Eel with its small eyes and round head. It is usually a dark brown color, but some are seen with reddish and greenish colors and fine black spots all over the body. Recently, albinos have become available in Japan. *P. dolloi* hibernates in summer like *P. annectens*. Also, in the past few years 5-10cm young specimens have become available for potential breeding stock at reasonable prices. No special care is needed. (Yamazaki)

Left: Spotted African Lungfish, *Protopterus dolloi*. **Below:** A young *Protopterus dolloi* still with its external gills.

An albino Spotted African Lungfish.

THE HIBERNATION OF *PROTOPTERUS ANNECTENS*

The dry season: When the rains stop and the heat rises sharply, small rivers and shallow ponds vanish into thin air. But before they are all gone, certain fishes migrate to large bodies of water, while others simply lay eggs that will survive the dry period, passing the genetic baton before succumbing to the heat and lack of water. At least four species of lungfish have another strategy, hibernation. When the rains return, the rivers flow and the ponds fill up again, and the lungfish stirs in its muddy bed.

1) The lungfish was released into 30cm of rice paddy mud covered with a thin layer of water.

2) The water was drained from the bottom of the container; eventually the lungfish stuck its mouth out of the water.

3) As the water disappeared, the lungfish sunk into the mud.

4) Even as the mud dried, the sound of breathing could occasionally be heard.

5) After a month the lungfish was dug up from the dried mud and found wrapped in a thin cocoon-like membrane. Its surface was dried out, but it was alive.

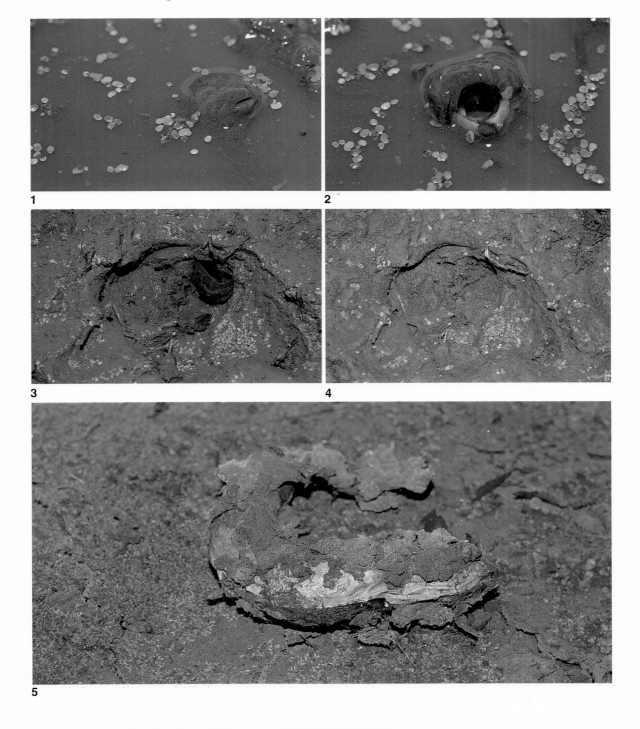

FRESHWATER STING RAYS

Of the rays (and their close relatives) that are known to inhabit fresh water, several species of stingrays from Southeast Asia and the large, widespread tropical Sawshark (nokogiri-ei) are well known, but these require a certain amount of salt water for aquarium raising, since problems arise if they are kept in fresh water for extended periods. The only rays that live exclusively in fresh water and can be kept indefinitely in a freshwater aquarium are those of the family Potamotrygonidae, which are distributed widely in South America.

The currently recognized two genera and 15 species of Potamotrygonidae are found in most of the waters of South America. However, like the catfishes, the rays come in various shapes and colors. Since it is often impossible to know just what region a species was collected in, and good reference works on these fishes are hard to come by, the identification of specimens often remains an unsolved mystery. So, if all one has is a photograph, usually it is anybody's guess as to what the species is. That is why we have left many identifications uncertain (*P.* sp.), unless the species is clearly identifiable.

Mottled Freshwater Stingray, *Potamotrygon hystrix*.

Mottled Freshwater Stingray (*Potamotrygon histrix*)

Found all over South America, including the Amazon, Orinoco, and La Plata River systems, this is the most common aquarium ray and the species that is usually displayed under the label "Amazonian freshwater stingray." A small ray with a disc diameter of 30cm, it is less expensive than most rays and perhaps suitable for beginners, but it is not especially hardier than the other species, so the aquarist should be very careful about water composition. (Kuroiwa)

Potamotrygon sp. cf. *histrix*

Small rays from the Amazon, such as this one, vary widely in color and markings. Judging from its size and shape, it is either a close relative of *P. histrix* or perhaps just a regional variation of it. Like *P. histrix*, it is sensitive to changes in water composition. (Kuroiwa)

Potamotrygon sp.

92

Potamotrygon sp.

This beautiful ray with a mosaic pattern and orange spotting inhabits the Amazon system. It has spines on its back, many in the center and others scattered about the edges. The spines on its tail are relatively big and sharp. The colorful spots in its eyes match the colors of its body spots. Recently, a larger number of this species has been imported. (Kuroiwa)

Orange-spotted Stingray (*Potamotrygon motoro*)

Distributed in the Amazon and La Plata Rivers, *P. motoro* is the second most common species after *P. histrix*. It is a beautiful ray with dark-bordered orange spots on a brown background. There are a lot of individual variations in these spots. A hardy species that is easy to raise, the Orange-spotted Stingray is the best one for beginners.

Left, top: *Potamotrygon* sp. **Left, bottom:** Orange-spotted Stingray, *Potamotrygon motoro*. **Below, top:** *Potamotrygon* sp. cf. *motoro*. **Below, bottom:** *Potamotrygon* sp.

Potamotrygon sp. cf. motoro

This species is believed to have been collected in the Uruguay or La Plata tributaries of the Amazon. The spines on its back are fairly dense, and its spots are smaller than those of *P. motoro*. It grows quickly, and judging from the fact that the sexual organs of a specimen of this species were smaller and less mature than those of a *P. motoro* of equal size, we can assume that it will grow significantly larger. A size of more than 60cm diameter can be expected of this hardy, easy-to-raise species. (Kuroiwa)

Potamotrygon sp.

This Amazonian species resembles the Orange-spotted Stingray, but its colors are lighter and the borders around its spots are ill-defined. It should reach a diameter of 40cm. (Kuroiwa)

Polka-dotted Stingray (*Potamotrygon* sp.)

Collected from the Xingu River, its smooth black body and white spots are striking for a ray, which usually has a yellow or brown coloration. There are three rows of spines along its tail, so it is definitely not a variation of a common species, all of which have a single row. This ray is hard to find in shops and when they are found they are expensive, but, fortunately, relatively easy to raise. The Polka-dotted Stingray will probably grow to 60cm diameter. (Kuroiwa)

Manta de Oro (*Potamotrygon* sp.)

This species is closely related to the previous one, but differs in several respects. This specimen's body color faded to a light brown, it has small spots around the perimeter of its body, and it has two rows of spines on its tail. It is not clear just how effective for identification purposes relying on the structure of the spines is, but it may work in some cases. The specimen pictured was collected from the Tocantins River. (Kuroiwa)

Above, top: Polka-dotted Stingray, *Potamotrygon* sp.
Above, bottom: Manta de Oro, *Potamotrygon* sp.
Left: Ahaya Grande, *Potamotrygon* sp.

Ahaya Grande (*Potamotrygon* sp.)

This very large species is found in the marshlands off the La Plata River. When I visited Paraguay, I saw an article in the local newspaper about a large specimen that had been caught which had a body thickness of 20cm. The Ahaya Grande is flatter than other species, with a blurry yellow and brown tortoise-shell pattern. Its skin is smooth, and its eyes are small for its body. Its short, flat tail is reminiscent of another species, *Disceus thayeri*. Very few Ahaya Grande are imported, but they present no special problems for aquarists besides their size. The amount a healthy specimen can eat is incredible. We hope that those who are lucky enough to acquire one will prepare a spacious tank and give it plenty of T.L.C. (Kuroiwa)

Note: I am indebted to Keishu Bisaku of the Tama Aquarium for his help in preparing these comments on rays.

94

RAISING THE BOWFIN (*AMIA CALVA*)

by Nobuhito Kuroiwa

TAXONOMY:

Like the gars, *Amia calva* is classified as a member of the Holosteans. Of the Holosteans, only the seven species of the genus *Lepisosteus* (gars) and this single species of *Amia* remain extant . The Holosteans are fundamentally distinguished from the Teleosts by their lower jaw construction: comparatively more bones comprise the Holostean lower jaw than the Teleostean lower jaw. The jaw structure of *Amia* is somewhat more like that of the Teleosts than it is like that of the gars, and it is considered a species that has branched off from the gars and main evolutionary line of the Holosteans.

RANGE:

The map provided shows the range of *Amia calva.* Except for Lake Superior, they can be found in the Great Lakes of North America and a broad area extending south from there. Fossils of the family Amiidae have also been excavated from deposits of the Cretaceous and Tertiary strata of Asia, Europe, and North America.

CHARACTERISTICS:

Most commonly known as the Bowfin, *Amia calva* also goes by a variety of regional names. In the

Geographic distribution of *Amia calva.*

Great Lakes it is called Dogfish, in the southern states Grinnell. It is a species that prefers to inhabit the gentle depths of lowland rivers, lakes lush with plant life, and various marshy or swampy areas, and tends to avoid places where the current is rough or the water especially turbid. Like the gar, *Amia* is equipped with an auxiliary air breathing capability, enabling it to survive where other carnivorous fishes cannot. In winter it is said to be able to live a day and a night out of the water. Extremely nocturnal in its habits, this meat-eater primarily feeds on various small fishes, such as sunfish, bass, perch, and minnow, as well as crayfish, frogs, and an assortment of insects.

The typical Bowfin reaches a length of about 60cm (though there have been reports of individual specimens reaching nearly one meter in length), with the female tending to be larger than the male. The male's caudal fin is provided with an ocellus (a black spot with vivid orange or yellow around its edges) at the upper base. On the sides of his body there is an irregular pattern, while his chest and pelvic and anal fins are for the most part green. In contrast, the female either lacks completely the ocellated spot sported by the male or exhibits a rather indistinct version of it. Likewise, the female's overall body color is quite plain in comparison to her male counterpart.

In its southern habitats, where the water temperature reaches about 25°C, the Bowfin begins spawning in April. In northern areas the breeding season begins later. When it comes time for breeding, the male moves into the shallows and uses water plants to build a light, round nest with a diameter of 25-50cm. Exhibiting his mating colors, he then will attempt to spawn with from one to several females.

Both the building of the nest and the spawning take place at night, at which time the female lays about 30,000 eggs of a sticky nature. The male acts as guardian, protecting the eggs and using his fins to send clean oxygenated water over them. The ocellated spot on the upper base of his caudal fin is believed to help ward off enemies at this time. In 8-10 days the eggs hatch. By way of a special cement organ on the head, the fry adhere to the nest wall and, bearing a large, hanging yolk sack, stay there for about 10 days. They then leave the nest, guided by the father, and eventually split up into small groups as they learn to swim. When they grow to about 10cm, they embark on a solitary life.

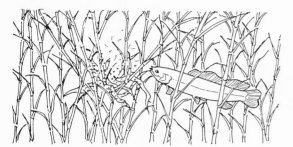

The Bowfin nest is built at breeding time.

In one year the young fish grow to over 20 cm, generally reaching lengths of more than 50cm in 5-6 years time. The natural life expectancy is 10 years, although there are records of *Amia* living over 30 years in captivity.

CARE:

Amia calva of 5-6cm length are imported into Japan from summer through autumn and can be purchased relatively inexpensively. Considering its short, stocky body, the Bowfin seems to be more reminiscent of the snakehead (*Channa* spp.) than it is of its relative the gar. In fact, except for the similar slight upward twist to its tail, the often quite violent fully-grown Bowfin has little in common with its particularly peaceful gar kin. That is not to say that the Bowfin lacks charm. On the contrary, the truly unique character of this fascinating fish can be seen especially when it is swimming with its dorsal fin undulating from just behind its head to the base of its caudal fin.

TANK:

While young, *Amia calva* are relatively peaceful, so raising them with other fishes is not particularly a problem. As they grow older, however, Bowfin become more and

more territorial and take to attacking presumed rivals, wreaking havoc on community tank life in the process. Rather than letting these fish get used to living in a group environment and then isolating them once they reach maturity and their aggressive natures start to show, it is best to prepare the Bowfin for life alone early by raising them in isolation from the beginning.

Though more predatory, the Bowfin grow less active as they get older. While the very young fish enjoy swimming about, their elders spend much of their time wallowing at the bottom of the tank, often not moving at all except to move a pectoral fin or lift a head. A very large tank is therefore unnecessary. For a fish raised by itself, a 90cm tank will do from the start, leaving plenty of room for growth.

To help the fish relax, it is a good idea to provide a shelter made out of an earthen pipe or something similar. If you are raising more than one smaller specimen together and there is room in the tank for more, you could go with a plant and stone layout, making it possible to add some arowanas or other upper level swimmers of the same size as your Bowfin.

FILTERS AND HEATING DEVICES: (See pages 33 & 34)

As with the gars, daily maintenance is important, and a powerful wet/dry or external filter is

1) Tubes and hoses securely fastened with stainless steel clamps. 2) Sandbag weight. 3) Lid. 4) Securely attached heating device. 5) Earthen pipe shelter. 6) Water level held several centimeters below lid.

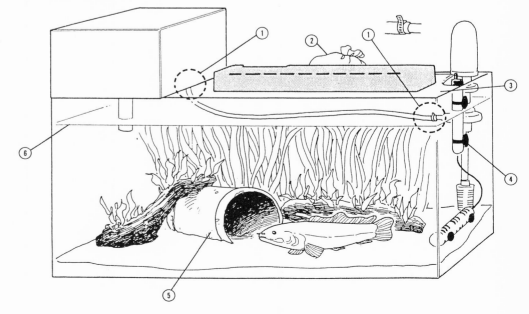

preferred. But be very careful, the nocturnal Bowfin are known for such nighttime mischief as detaching hoses or tubes and jumping out of tanks. To avoid such accidents, it is important to make sure that the tank is set up very securely. The filter box and the hose connected to the pump should be fastened with stainless steel and secured tightly with a clamp. Great care should also be given to installing the thermostat and heater securely in a corner. You can cover the tank with a very sturdy, heavy, plastic, but remember to put something heavy on top of it to hold it in place. It is also essential to leave several centimeters of space between the water's surface and the lid since, like the gars, the Bowfin occasionally comes up to the surface for air.

MAINTENANCE:

Because it is such a strong breeder, *Amia calva* is a familiar fixture in the areas that it inhabits. Famous for its extraordinary vitality, it is a fish that can survive in wetlands where others cannot. These are truly hardy fish that do not die easily. Even in captivity, barring any external injuries that full-grown specimens might sustain from such nighttime antics as jumping out of the tank or fights, they can be kept for a very long time.

As fish whose natural distribution spans all the way from the Great Lakes to the Florida peninsula, *Amia calva* are thought to be fairly adaptable to changes in water temperature. However, young specimens imported into Japan during the summer seem to be an exception. Not yet used to high water temperatures or changes in water quality, they tend to die easily. So, until the specimens are fully mature, appropriate caution is suggested.

If you are raising your Bowfin with tropical fishes, the temperature should be kept above 28°C for the sake of the other fishes. However, even in winter it is not necessary to keep the water heated for *Amia* alone. There are no special concerns about water quality here, but to preserve the pH in the slightly acidic to slightly alkaline range, you should change ⅓ of the water once every 10 days and clean the filter once a month. Doing so will help stop problems before they start. In the same respect, it is important to remove any uneaten food immediately, since leftover food is the leading cause of deterioration of the water quality.

A young Bowfin. The caudal fin ocellus can be seen.

SICKNESS:

When raising *Amia calva*, there is no particular sickness to watch out for. However, if you are raising multiple animals, there is always the risk of external injuries sustained in the process of seizing and defending territories. If this should occur, transfer the wounded fish to another tank and administer a treatment such as Green F Gold as a medicinal bath. As a precautionary measure, I suggest using less than the dosage prescribed. These fish are quite sensitive to chemical substances, to the extent that "treatment" with some medications can be life-threatening. Once the fish has completely recovered, it is not wise to put it back into the mixed tank lest the same thing happen again. At this point, arranging for solitary raising is probably the answer.

FOOD AND FEEDING:

Amia calva is said to be a gluttonous carnivore. Small fishes and crustaceans always make good food, but it doesn't take long for them to get used to eating and enjoying frozen shrimp, sliced meat, and even processed foods such as krill. Their large appetites, however, can prompt overfeeding, which in turn can lead to deterioration of water quality, sickness, and finally death of the fish. Similarly, an unvaried diet, even if they seem to like it, seems related to a shortened life span for the fish. In order to assure you and your fish many happy years together, it is best to underfeed a little and keep the diet balanced and varied.

BREEDING:

The Bowfin's breeding requirements are considered to be extremely difficult to recreate in an aquarium, and to the best of my knowledge it has never been done. But if you were to put a well-matched pair into a tank of 180cm or more, adjust the temperature relative to the changes in the seasons, and provide the plant life necessary for making the nest, it would probably be possible. Pond breeding seems relatively easier, since Japan lies on the same latitude as the Bowfin's natural habitat. Chances are, spawning the Bowfin in an aquarium isn't long in coming, considering how its unique breeding style has the interest of so many aquarists, including mine.

DANGER OF NATURALIZATION:

Should you become tired of raising fishes and bored with keeping an aquarium, don't ever give in to the impulse to set them free in a nearby river. For some this may seem a tempting, harmless alternative. As fishes that make their home in the temperate and subtropical areas of North America, the gars and the Bowfin could possibly adapt, flourish, and breed quite easily in Japan's swamps or rivers. As a matter of fact, there have recently been rumored sightings of gars in some of the swamplands of Japan. But this is not good news. Today, so many of those rivers in Japan that are home to freshwater fishes are being lost, made unfit for life by the hands of man. Imagine what will happen if the number of omnivorous fishes increases in these places? If you truly are a fish-loving aquarist, it is your responsibility to think of these things. Setting these fishes free is simply a selfish solution to a problem that should have been considered before deciding to raise fishes in the first place.

REFERENCES:

Howes, G. J. 1987. The Amia and Gar Pike. in Animal Encyclopedia, Vol. 13, *Fish.* K. E. Bannister, ed., under the supervision of Iwai Tamotsu. Heibon-sha. pp. 28-29.

Nikolsky, G. B. & Takai Akihiro. 1982. *Ichthyological Taxonomy,* Third Edition, Revised and Enlarged. Tatara Shobo.

Pflieger, William L. 1975. *The Fishes of Missouri.* Missouri Dept. of Conservation, Jefferson City. 343pp.

Tomelleri, Joseph R. & Mark E. Eberele. 1990. *Fishes of the Central United States.* Univ. of Kansas Press. 300pp.

Uchida, Kiyoshi. 1963. *Animal Taxonomy, (I) Vertebrates, (Ia) Fishes.* Nakayama Shoten.

RAISING GARS

by Nobuhito Kuroiwa

TAXONOMY:

The gars, along with *Amia calva*, are known as survivors of those Holosteans that reached their prime from the Jurassic period to the beginning of the Cretaceous period. According to E.O. Wiley (1972), there are two genera of gars, *Altractosteus* and *Lepisosteus*. Although some references consider the gars to be classified into only the single genus *Lepisosteus*, for our purposes Wiley's distinction still holds.

The two genera presently include seven extant species. Belonging to the genus *Atractosteus* are three species that are known as the Manfaris in Japan (although the real Manfari is the Cuban Gar): the Alligator Gar (*A. spatula*), the Cuban Gar (*A. tristoechus*), and the Tropical Gar (*A. tropicus*). Of the genus *Lepisosteus*, four species are known: the Shortnose Gar (*L. platostomos*), the Longnose Gar (*L. osseus*), the Spotted Gar (*L. oculatus*), and the Florida Spotted Gar (*L. platyrhincus*).

There is a great deal of difference between the genera *Atractosteus* and *Lepisosteus* in terms of number of gill rakers and width of the mouth. But the easiest way to distinguish between them on sight in an aquarium is by comparing the upper jaw length (S in the photo) with the head length without the upper jaw (H in the photo). In this picture of the head of the Tropical Gar you can clearly see that the upper jaw length (H) is greater.

Especially with very young fishes, distinguishing between them can be difficult—so difficult that often the Spotted Gar and the Shortnose Gar are mistakenly sold as the Alligator Gar. To be on the safe side, you are better off learning to make the distinction yourself. On this page a key to the species of gars has been provided.

RANGE:

The maps on these pages show where the seven species are primarily located. Today, gars are found naturally in North and Central America, but fossils have been found in Europe, Africa, and India. The Tropical Gar and Cuban Gar are generally found in tropical areas near the equator; the Florida Spotted Gar inhabits the U.S. from the Florida peninsula to the southern Georgian lowlands; the Alligator Gar, Longnose Gar, Shortnose Gar, and Spotted Gar thrive in an area centering around the Mississippi River. Of these, the Longnose Gar is known to inhabit the broadest area, residing as far north as the Canadian province of Quebec.

KEY TO THE GARS:

A_1 (H) longer than (S); over 59 gill rakers .... *Atractosteus* species

    B_1 Less than 56 lateral line scales; body color like the Longnose Gar .... Tropical gar (*A. tropicus*)

    B_2 More than 56 lateral line scales

        C_1 Body entirely black with irregular pattern; 59-66 gill rakers ... .Alligator Gar (*A. spatula*)

        C_2 Mature fish with an unpatterned brownish green body; 67-81 gill rakers; very broad bite.............. Cuban Gar (*A. tristoechus*)

A_2 (H) either shorter than (S) or equal to it; 33 or fewer gill rakers .... *Lepisosteus* species

    B_1 (S) about twice (H) .... Longnose Gar (*L. osseus*)

    B_2 (H) either a little shorter than or equal to (S)

        C_1 Head without spotted pattern; 59-65 lateral line scales.......... .... Shortnose Gar (*L. platostomus*)

        C_2 Head with spotted pattern; 53-59 lateral line scales

            D_1 A few small plates on isthmus; not found in peninsular Florida .... Spotted Gar (*L. oculatus*)

Gill arch of a gar (specimen provided by Matsushima Aquarium).

BEHAVIOR:

The particulars of environment and lifestyle vary depending upon the species, but for the most part gars prefer to live in places where the current is slow. Rivers, marshes, or lakes with stagnant water suit them best. Mature fish inhabit relatively deep places, while the young tend to move toward the shores of rivers where there is lush plant life. Upon occasion, gars have been known to live in brackish areas. The Alligator Gar has even been accused of slipping into fishing ports and causing trouble, like breaking fishing lines.

Spawning behavior also varies according to species. The explanation provided here uses the Longnose Gar as an example.

In the last ten days of April, the full-grown Longnose Gar starts to move upstream to the clear water rapids (it is said that the Longnose Gar can swim extremely fast). From the last 10 days of May to the middle of June is spawning season. At first a single female (generally the larger of the two sexes) snuggles up with several males to form a small group. She then proceeds to separate from the group repeatedly in order to lay some eggs and then she rejoins them. At the river bottom she makes a depression or bed by stirring up the sand with her caudal fin and laying the eggs there. Meanwhile, a few of the males snuggle up to her and encourage the spawning by stimulating her at the tip of her snout. (The Longnose Gar has occasionally been known to lay its eggs in the nest of the Smallmouth Bass, in which case the male Smallmouth Bass is said to protect the eggs and hatchlings.)

Some say that the spawning process is so vigorous that even from very far away you can hear the tell-tale sounds of splashing and fins slapping on the

water all through the spawning season.

The eggs hatch in 6-8 days. The newly-hatched fry have a large yolk sac and mucous covering on the tip of their snout that sticks fast to anything it touches. Once the yolk sac is used up, the fry feed on any mosquito larvae and small crustaceans they can catch. As they mature, they move on to killifishes and eventually start hunting larger fish. Throughout the summer the hatchlings stay put, growing to nearly 50cm after one year.

Once they mature, 90% of their diet is fish. The remaining 10% is shrimp, crayfish, and other freshwater crustaceans and various insects that fall onto the water's surface. The biggest gar, the Alligator Gar, is said to sometimes prey on waterfowl.

The male Longnose Gar reaches maturity in 3-4 years and grows to

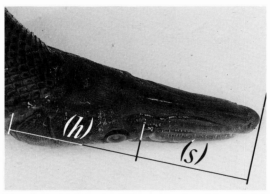

Head of the Tropical Gar showing (h) and (s) proportions.

about 90cm in length. The female reaches maturity in about 6 years, at a length of about 140cm. In the case of the Spotted Gar, the male grows faster for the first two years. During his 2nd to 3rd year he reaches about 50cm and then stops growing completely. The female continues to grow at least through her fourth year, sometimes even beyond that. Compared to the

Left: Range of the Alligator Gar. **Right:** Range of the Shortnose Gar.

100

male, she grows more slowly, but there have been cases of individual specimens reaching 110cm. Besides size, there isn't really any other external characteristic by which to distinguish the male gar from the female.

CARE:

Raising a primitive fish like the gar, whose appearance hasn't changed since the Mesozoic Era, isn't particularly difficult. This extremely vigorous fish is tough to kill unless one makes a very big mistake. But, in order to really appreciate the charm of these fishes and experience the joy of raising them, you have to start with the right mental attitude. You've got to ask yourself a few things like how much time are you willing to devote to the task, and how long are you willing to devote time and money to maintaining the necessary equipment. A primitive fish like the gar will live peacefully in its natural environment for over 10 years. Some of those raised in modern Japanese aquariums,

Top: Ranges of three species of gars. **1)** Florida Spotted Gar. **2)** Cuban Gar. **3)** Tropical Gar. **Bottom, left:** Range of the Longnose Gar. **Bottom, right:** Range of the Spotted Gar.

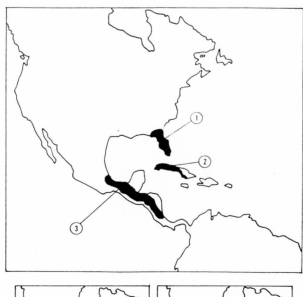

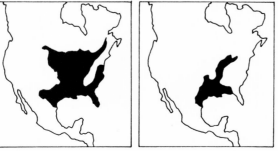

however, are still living after 25 years. These fishes are not going to quit early; you have got to be sure you are not going to either. It is better not to begin at all if the fish is eventually going to be abandoned to die later, anyway.

To add to the trouble of raising them, gars are generally large fishes. Even a small-sized species like the Spotted Gar can reach 60cm in captivity. For a fish like the Longnose Gar, whose snout is its longest part, a particularly wide tank is necessary. And the exceptionally long Alligator Gar certainly is not going to live comfortably in a typical easy-to-deal-with private tank. Even in their natural habitats Alligator Gar are scarce, so it is not surprising to find that they are not imported into Japan in large numbers. When they are abundant enough to be imported, there is always the fear that nearly all of them will die as a result of neglectful aquarists who finally abandon them. Still, if you are resolved to enjoy the company of a gar for a long time, it is essential that you obtain and set up the proper equipment and not set impossible goals. Instead of concentrating on trying to find the most exotic species to raise, you should consider how much and what kind of equipment each particular fish needs and whether or not you can provide it, as well as how long you plan to keep the fish. If possible, you should do some research into the breeding and raising method that is best for you. A custom-made plan often leads to the most enjoyment.

TANK:

As stated before, the gar requires a fairly large tank. Even Spotted Gar need a tank of at least 90cm, though that size can house up to three mature specimens. A deep tank is preferred. A depth of about 60cm would allow you to raise most large specimens. However, when it comes to the Longnose Gar, it is difficult to say whether even a 180cm tank would ultimately suffice. And even the smallest Alligator Gar would eventually require a tank about 2m X 1m X 1m.

If there is no way you can prepare a wide enough tank, you should at least stick to a simple layout. Securing plenty of open space for swimming should be the top priority. You also have to leave enough room at the top of the tank so that the gar can occasionally surface for air. Beware, these fishes tend to jump out of the water, so don't forget to provide a secure lid.

COHABITATION:

If possible, solitary raising is preferred. Rather than attacking other fishes, it is the gars gentle nature to nestle up to them. Large South American catfishes and arowanas are often its tank companions, but this is not necessarily a happy situation for the gars. These fishes drive the poor gar crazy with menacing behavior so that it winds up spending most of its time with its nose rubbing up against the side of the tank, unable to relax and swim about freely. But if you

Southern Pike with *Vallisneria* growing in the background.

A pleco (*Pseudacanthicus* sp.) living with a gar requires constant attention.

really want to raise your gar with other fishes, your best bet is to house them with the Northern Pike — also a peaceful North American species — in a spacious tank with plenty of tall water plants such as *Vallisneria*.

One thing is for sure, even if the other fishes are fellow gars, they should all be pretty much the same size. In cases where there is a substantial size discrepancy, broken noses or wounded lower jaws often result from one fish accidentally biting the snout of another at feeding time. This has been known to happen, particularly in the young Longnose

Gar at the point where its snout is thinnest, so sufficient caution should be exercised. Other problem tankmates for the gars are the large plecos. These fishes have been known to harass the timid gar all night long, in the worst cases resulting in its death. If you insist on keeping a pleco, your best bet is a sailfin pleco that is big enough to not be eaten by a gar. These fishes are used as tank cleaners; they eat algae and keep the glass clear of it. There can be problems like those mentioned above with these catfishes, too.

FILTRATION:

Generally you want to use a wet/dry or exterior filter that is as powerful as possible. With carnivores like the gars, if the filter isn't strong enough the water quickly becomes dirty and, as I will discuss later, feeding them becomes impossible. You should use a filter with a broad surface because it doesn't clog up easily. Two new products on the market are a ping-pong ball-shaped item made out of a porous ceramic material, and a vinyl chloride item, either of which you can use. Spreading a wool mat on top and changing it regularly also helps keep the filter in good condition for a longer period of time. If you use a filter made of clear material you can easily tell when it is becoming dirty, which makes maintenance easier.

MAINTENANCE:

Spotted Gar inhabit murky swamp areas that ordinary fishes do not (or cannot). Thanks to its air breathing ability, it can survive in waters where the oxygen content is fairly low. Since there are species like the Longnose Gar that are found in areas from the tropical to the sub-arctic zone (in terms of Japan's latitudes, this means an area extending from Okinawa to Hokkaido), you can say that these are fishes with a strong ability to adapt to all sorts of water compositions and temperatures. As a result, even in an aquarium no special precautions are necessary. As long as you prepare a good set-up from the start, you can pretty much enjoy carefree maintenance in the future.

When deciding on the water temperature, however, it is a good idea to consider the natural environment of your particular species. In an order progressing from north to south, there's the Longnose Gar, Spotted Gar, Shortnose Gar, Alligator Gar, Florida Spotted Gar, and Tropical Gar. For the Longnose Gar, found as far north as Canada, even a little lower than 0°C is fine, while for the Tropical Gar, which only resides in the tropical regions of Central America, the temperature should not drop below 18°C.

If you are thinking of raising your gar with other tropical fishes, a temperature of about 20-26°C is best. Again, these fishes are for the most part extremely adaptable. Even on a hot summer's day when the temperature rises above 30°C, as long as the water conditions do not deteriorate the heat is not a problem.

When raising species like the Longnose Gar and the Spotted Gar, which inhabit cold areas, it should not

protein from leftover food breaks down into ammonia and nitrites both of which are known to be harmful to most fishes, particularly due to a strain on the respiratory system. Thanks to the gars ability to breathe air they are often able to survive in an aquarium where other fishes die as a result of this. However, if such deteriorated water conditions are allowed to continue, even the most robust gars will end up suffering from accumulated stress. They may not die right away, but their lives will most likely be shortened as a result. Since it is often impossible to detect such water deterioration by simply looking at the surface, it is imperative that aquarists constantly run tests to look out for this problem.

Proper maintenance involves

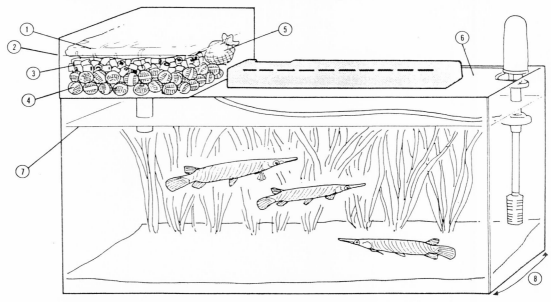

1) Floss pad. 2) Separator. 3) Ceramic beads. 4) Bio-balls. 5) Chemical resin bag. 6) Lid. 7) Water level kept several centimeters below top. 8) Keep proper front to back tank depth.

be necessary to keep the water heated even in winter. As the water temperature goes down, their appetites tend to follow suit and the fishes may take to lying on the bottom without moving. Do not be alarmed, this is quite natural behavior and may also be linked to breeding behavior. You could also raise these fishes in a garden pond, but if you do you must keep in mind the fact that they are air breathers. In the winter season it is important to construct some mechanism to prevent the water surface from freezing over.

The gars can endure quite admirably when it comes to deterioration of water quality. The

keeping the pH in a range from 6.5-7.5 and changing one-third of the water once every 10 days. Although it depends somewhat on the strength of the filter, most tanks should be cleaned out once a month. Also, if you put some large grain coral sand in the filter box, you can ameliorate some of the extreme oxidation that accompanies water deterioration. Compared to other fishes, the gar is not particularly sensitive to the water-changing process. If this is carried out quickly, using hot water from a kettle or such to adjust the temperature, it shouldn't be a problem. As cold-blooded animals, sudden changes in water temperature can cause fishes great stress. Neutralizing the water immediately really is necessary.

It is important to regularly carry out maintenance as described above. As time goes by, you will become more and more able to tell the condition of the water by the fish's appetite, body color, and behavior. But for the busy fishkeeper who doesn't have time to pay such close attention to his charges, or for the beginning aquarist, keeping a calendar is a good idea, so as not to forget when to change the water.

SICKNESSES:

To the best of my knowledge, there is no particular disease you have to watch out for when raising gars. But once in a while they do fall victim to parasites that reach them by way of the small live fishes that they feed on. When this happens, you have two options for treatment. The first is direct removal. This means taking the infested specimen out of the tank and, without harming the outer skin, restraining it with a soft, moist hand towel and directly removing the parasite(s) with tweezers. (Unlike most fishes, the gars will not immediately grow weak when removed from the tank.) The second method is to use a medicinal treatment. This is not the best choice for young specimens, considering that most primitive fishes, including the gars, have a low tolerance for medicines. But when the specimen is too large to easily remove from the tank, medicine is the only treatment. Start with a diluted dosage, about one-twentieth of the prescribed amount. If it appears to have no effect, strengthen the dosage while watching the fish for results. Since with either method there is some risk involved, you should practice preventive care by making a point of regularly checking the food for such parasites.

FOOD:

Similar to land animals, fishes need a nutritious diet to grow properly, which means a simple combination of proteins, fats, carbohydrates, and vitamins. Fishes especially require a lot of protein in their diet, 2-3 times more than land animals do.

As mentioned earlier, the gar is basically a hunting carnivore in its natural habitat. For feeding those in captivity, a diet of primarily small fishes, enhanced with crustaceans like

brine shrimp and krill, is desirable. In keeping with its natural eating habits, some say that it is a good idea to offer them insect food occasionally, like the crickets sold as reptile food. One thing you should not do, however, is to always give your fish the same type of food. Variety is the key to a balanced diet.

If you cannot obtain small fishes to use for food, or if this is just not economically feasible, you can try fresh fishes such as rainbow trout or smelt (frozen is okay). At the Tama Aquarium, where the tank is large, the filter effective, and the overall system top-grade, this sort of food is

Gar eating processed food.

commonly used. Fresh fish is good because of its high protein and amino acid content, but can cause problems if it is not fresh enough since the fat it contains is easily oxidized. Oxidized fat tends to make the fish's vitamin consumption increase, which is known to cause anemia, stunted growth, and liver problems. (Even the fat of frozen fishes oxidizes.) Ultimately, it is best to use extremely fresh fish whenever possible and always remember to remove leftover food from the tank immediately. It is possible to get your fish accustomed to ready-mixed food made specifically for large fishes. This is a particularly good choice if your filter is not very efficient.

At public aquariums, the standard daily food amount is equal to from 1-3% of the total body weight of the fishes. For a home aquarium, considering the width of the tank and the efficiency of the filter, a bit less than this will do. But remember, growth rate depends upon food intake,

104

so particularly in the beginning stages it is important to feed the fishes enough. Malnutrition when the fish are young can lead to malformation of the backbone. You should also consider the width of the snout when deciding the amount of food. Species with a narrow snout, like the Longnose Gar, can suffer from heavy feeding.

Since gars tend to drift slowly at the water's surface, floating food is most suitable. In a tank with only gars, they will somewhat clumsily swim down to snatch up any food that may fall to the tank bottom. But in a mixed tank you should make sure that the meat-eaters dwelling in the lower depths are not the only ones getting fed.

RAISING THE YOUNG:

Gars generally lay their eggs in June. At around the same time, newly-hatched specimens of about 5 centimeters are imported into Japan off and on. Lately, not only the Spotted Gar, but specimens of the larger Shortnose Gar and the Longnose Gar are also imported. Due to troublesome similarities between the species, there are many cases of specimens being mistakenly sold under the wrong name.

Raising the fish from such a young age is extremely interesting, but you must be careful. They are not nearly so resistant to disease and harmful surroundings as they are later in life. You should start off by feeding them bloodworms and minnows. As they mature you can go from killifishes to various other small fishes. Then, little by little, move on to processed food alternating with the sort of food previously described. Again, as they mature the fish will have a surprisingly large appetite, and it is important to

1) Filter outlet faces into tank creating current. 2) Lid. 3) Sponge filter. 4) Keep water at 23°C.

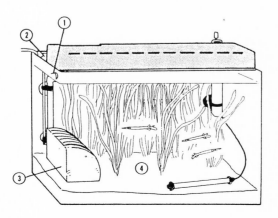

Group of young gar, *Lepisosteus osseus.*

feed them enough to keep them growing quickly. Furthermore, if the tank is too large the young fish will not be able to catch enough food. A 60cm tank is just about right.

As for the filtering system, a bottom filter is okay, but live foods may get sucked into it; to prevent this from happening a sponge filter is better. In preparing the layout, you should keep in mind that the young gar are not yet very good at swimming, so your set-up should not create strong currents. A moderate amount of plant life is a good idea to help reduce stress in the fishes. You also have to be more attentive to water quality when raising young fish compared to full-grown specimens. When changing the water, pre-boiled water should be used. Keep the water at about 23°C and avoid abrupt changes in temperature.

BREEDING:

To the best of my knowledge, breeding has not been documented outside of the public aquarium. Several years ago, Longnose Gar were bred in the Suma Aquarium of Japan (now Suma Seaside Marine Park). The fish hatched at that time are still alive today.

Gars are not generally bred in captivity for a variety of reasons. First of all, it takes about four years for a fish to reach breeding age. It is also difficult to tell the difference between males and females, as well as to recreate the seasonal climate of the temperate zone that they are used to. Yet, ironically, the gars gentle demeanor and robust health are generally accepted as the main deterrents to breeding. Since it is a fish that can cohabitate with ease, it is usually kept with other tropical fishes, so it rarely has enough space to engage in reproductive behavior.

But since Japan is at just about the same latitude as the gars natural North American habitat, and a pond

105

makes for a very wide environment, several specimens can be kept in ponds for years on end without even the need for heating. It is not unreasonable to think that these conditions will result in numerous opportunities for breeding.

ACQUISITION:

Prize-winning specimens from each of the seven extant species of gars, except for the Cuban Gar (Manfari) and Florida Spotted Gar, have been imported into Japan. In the past there have been gars raised at the Ueno Aquarium and the Yomiuri Land-Sea Aquarium, but none were prize winning specimens.

It is difficult to tell whether Florida Spotted Gar or Spotted Gar have been imported because they resemble one another so much in external appearance. Since the Florida Spotted Gar is only found from Florida to the southern lowlands of Georgia, where the Spotted Gar is not, we should be able to get a definitive answer based on which region they were imported from. For additional confirmation, there is the fact that the Florida Spotted Gar is said to grow to 130cm, a bit larger than the Spotted Gar which reaches only 60 cm in captivity. But I, who have, regretfully, never observed a living specimen, do not know for certain.

Almost all of the prized specimens brought into Japan are members of the genus *Lepisosteus*. A few have been Tropical Gar and Alligator Gar, both species of the genus *Altractosteus*, but not many. Spotted Gar, Longnose Gar, and Shortnose Gar, all *Lepisosteus* species, are constantly being imported into Japan and are relatively easy to get. If you do not have an especially large tank, of the three I recommend either the Spotted Gar or the Shortnose Gar. The Spotted Gar has been especially popular for a long time. Its beautiful body color and distinct pattern variations between specimens lend it a unique charm and make it fun to choose a favorite. The body design changes as the fish matures. For example, in many cases the young fish will have a dark, intricate pattern on its stomach that changes to a white, less-detailed, and larger-style design by the time it is fully grown.

One important thing to look for when choosing a specimen is a tendency to relax at the water surface. You should avoid fish that are swimming about wildly and banging their noses against the tank walls. If continued for a while, this sort of behavior often turns into a vicious cycle of injury as the fish constantly rubs its injured snout against the glass until, finally, in the end the snout is either permanently damaged or broken. So as not to harm the snout when handling the fish, you should always chase them around cautiously with a proper sized net and scoop them up with great care. A large vinyl net works best.

Also, when you are buying a fish from a tank stocked with many specimens, be on the look-out for missing fins or damaged eyes among the fish. Buying an already injured fish is not unheard of.

REFERENCES:

Harajima, Ichio. 1978. Warm-water Fresh-Water Fish Food. in *The Care Handbook–Breeding, Raising, and Illness*. Aquarium Edition. Japan Zoo and Aquarium Society. p.51-53

Hatai, Yushio & Shibada Ogawa. 1991. *Recognizing and Remedying Fish Illnesses*. Nihon Dobutsu Yakuhin Company.

Page, L. M. & B. M. Burr. 1991. *A Field Guide to Freshwater Fishes*. Houghton Mifflen Co., Boston.

Pflieger, W. L. 1975. *The Fishes of Missouri*. Missouri Dept. of Conservation.

Sato, Tetsu. 1992. The Behavior of Others as the Environment. *in* Shibatani, Nagano, and Yoro, eds. *Lectures on Evolution 7. From Ecology to Evolution*. Tokyo University Publications, p.208-211.

Tomelleri, J. R. & M. E. Eberle. 1990. *Fishes of the Central United States*. Kansas Univ. Press.

Uchida, Kiyoshi. 1963. *Animal Taxonomy, 9: Vertebrates, (Ia) Fish*. Nakayama Shoten.

Wiley, E. O. 1976. The Phylogeny and Biogeography of Fossil and Recent Gars (Actinopterygii: Lepisosteidae). Univ. Kansas Mus. Nat. Hist., Misc. Publ. 4. 111pp.

Williams, J. D., et al. 1983. *The Audobon Field Guide to North American Fishes, Whales & Dolphins*. Alfred A. Knopf. New York.

RAISING *POLYPTERUS*

by Koichi Yamazaki

Head on view of a *Polypterus* species.

TAXONOMY:

One of the results of Napoleon's push into Egypt was the discovery of *Polypterus*. Accompanying the army was E. Geoffroy Saint Hilaire of the Paris Museum of Natural History, who discovered in the Nile a one-meter-long green fish that very much resembled the gar. Its back was lined with small fins, and he named it *Polypterus*. This generic name means "many fins," and expresses the fish's most distinctive character. The French scholar of natural history, Cuvier, praised the event, saying words to the effect that, "If only for the discovery of this fish, the invasion of Egypt was worthwhile." In 1802, the scientific name *Polypterus bichir* was given at a scholarly conference by Saint Hilaire.

Later, further research was carried out on the classification and today there are two genera in the family Polypteridae, *Polypterus* and *Erpetoichthys* (which used to be called *Calamoichthys*). There are 9 or 10 species, some of which having subspecies, of *Polypterus*, and only one known species of *Erpetoichthys*. *Erpetoichthys* can be distinguished by its characteristic elongate body shape and lack of pelvic fins.

Ichthyologists have had difficulty classifying the different species of *Polypterus* because they share so many different characteristics with other primitive fish groups. The swim bladder is transformed into a lung-like organ split horizontally into two sections and so brings the lungfishes to mind. The hard scales, called ganoid scales, harken back to the the gars of the Holosteans. The externally protruding nostrils are reminiscent of *Amia calva*. The spiracle behind the eye and the spiral intestinal tract are shared with cartilaginous fishes and *Acipenser*. The head, jaw bone, and pectoral fins, which are fleshy "handles" supported by a bony framework, are similar to *Latimeria*. In the past, as a result of this confusion, they were classified as Crossopterygians, but recently the accepted classification is in the subclass Branchiopterygii.

107

RANGE:

Polypterus species live only in the fresh waters of Africa, in a range limited to East, Central, and West Africa. In the eastern part they are primarily found in the Nile River system, where we have *P. bichir* and *P. endlicheri*, and the still unnamed Nile River subspecies of *P. senegalus*. *P. senegalus* and *P. bichir* have also been reported to occur in Lake Turkana (Lake Rudolf).

In the central part of Africa, many different species thrive in the Zaire

Fishermen at Lake Tanganyika, Africa.

River System. This includes various subspecies of *P. endlicheri*, such as *P. e. congicus*, as well as *P. ornatipinnis*, *P. delhezi*, *P. palmas*, *P. retropinnis*, and *P. polli*. *P. congicus* and *P. ornatipinnis* are also found in Lake Tanganyika. In the Katanga Region upstream, where various rivers come together, there are *P. bichir katangae*, *P. senegalus meridionalis* and *P. weeksii*.

In West Africa, the main range is the Niger River System where *P. endlicheri*, *P. bichir lapradei*, *P. senegalus* and *Erpetoichthys calabaricus* are found. *P. bichir lapradei* and *P. senegalus* are also found in the Senegal and Gambia Rivers. In Liberia, there are *P. palmas* and *P. retropinnis lowei*, and in Guinea there is *P. ansorgei*.

BEHAVIOR:

Polypterus species, which are able to breathe by use of their "lungs," primarily like to live in areas where the bottom is muddy, the water shallow, and the water plants flourishing. Nocturnal in habit, they swim about very actively at night.

They feed on small fishes and amphibians as well as, occasionally, crustaceans and other large invertebrates. Behavior doesn't change much in captivity. At night, when the fluorescent lamp in the tank is turned off, if you watch them vigilantly enough you can often catch sight of them making their way to the water surface to snort a breath of air and hunt for food.

Young Bichirs have a pair of long, vertically held external gills covered with soft filaments as seen in amphibians and lungfishes. But, regardless of the species, as they mature they lose them and come to rely on breathing air. *Polypterus* species use their unusual pectoral fins, which are of a fleshy quality supported by a distinctive bone structure, to support themselves on and even to crawl across the bottom. Even on land, *Polypterus* can get around quickly, much like a lizard, by stumping around on its pectoral fins.

For differences between the sexes and   other information regarding breeding, please refer to the section on propagation.

CARE:
Acquiring *Polypterus* and Preparing to Raise Them:

It is a very happy moment when you finally spot a specimen that strikes your fancy at the pet store. It is even more thrilling when you are choosing among the *Polypterus* whose specimens, even of the same species, exhibit extreme differences in body color and pattern, as well as facial expression — if you look closely enough.

When choosing your specimen, the first thing to do is check all parts of the body for irregularities, such as injury or deformities. For parts of the fin that can grow back, like the filaments, it's a judgment call. But it is best to avoid specimens when there is damage to a part that cannot grow back, like the eyeball or the operculum. You should also be wary of specimens whose dorsal fins have been cut or bitten off at their base — these will not grow back!

Next, you will probably want to choose a fish based on pattern, body color, facial expression, and shape, which is simply a question of personal taste and needs little

A *Polypterus delhezi* with its many distinct dorsal fins.

comment here. We touched upon general esthetics in the color photo section a little. But, more than beauty, it is important to consider the extremely long life-span of species of *Polypterus* when taking on the responsibility of raising one.

As you will now see, it is not a particularly difficult feat to raise *Polypterus*. For the most part, it requires basic equipment and maintenance. Abraham Lincoln said that when a man turns forty, how responsibly he has lived shows in his face. I would like to say that after 10 years, how responsibly a *Polypterus* has been raised shows in its face and body. The fish wears the effects of the equipment used and maintenance carried out. A poorly fed specimen may suffer from curvature of the spine or bulging eyes or take on a rounded, plump look. Slipshod maintenance can cause repeated facial injuries or broken snouts, which in turn often leads to declining enthusiasm for raising the fish.

But *Polypterus* nurtured carefully in a properly maintained environment will mature steadily and eventually make a fine addition to any aquarist's collection.

CHOOSING THE TANK:

Having divided the *Polypterus* into three rankings according to size and categorizing the species, we can come up with the smallest possible tank for a fully-grown fish of each species. (The following species include only the species of *Polypterus* presently being raised in Japan.)

The large-sized group includes fishes over 50cm, such as *P. endlicheri*, *P. palmas congicus* and *P. ornatipinnis*. In this case you want to prepare a tank of 120cm or more. The middle-sized group reaches about 40cm and includes *P. bichir lapradei*, *P. weeksii*, *P. delhezi*, and *P.*

retropinnis lowei. They need a tank of at least 90cm. Finally, there is the smallest group, which grow to about 30cm, and includes *P. senegalus*, *P. p. palmas*, *P. polli*, *P. retropinnis*, and *Erpetoichthys*. A 60cm or larger tank is good for these species.

It is okay to take into account a margin for growth when preparing a tank, although one rule of thinking says that it is better to increase the size of the tank in stages, one step at a time, as the fish grows. This way the tank is never too big or too small. If the *Polypterus* feels extremely hemmed in, it tends to lose its composure and swim about recklessly in something like a mild state of shock. This can bring about injuries or accidents from leaping out of the tank. A tank that is too large can also cause problems with stalking live food. It is my opinion that if you are starting with hatchlings or adolescent fish, it is best to follow the one-step-up rule.

SETTING:

Above all, you want to establish a stable foundation for the tank. *Polypterus* are very sensitive to vibrations. If you set up the tank in a place where people are always walking back and forth, the fish will feel the vibrations and most likely become very agitated. In time self-inflicted injuries, from something like jumping out of the tank, could result. For preventive measures, be sure to reinforce the bottom of the tank by putting something like a styrofoam board between the tank and whatever it is standing on. This will at least absorb some of the vibrations.

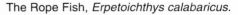

The Rope Fish, *Erpetoichthys calabaricus*.

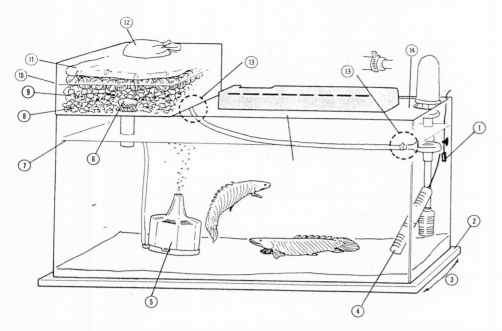

1) Battery operated thermostatic sensor. 2) Styrofoam buffer. 3) Plenty of depth. 4) Free-floating covered heater. 5) Supplementary filter and aerator. 6) Net covering. 7) Water level a little low. 8) Large grain coral sand. 9) Ceramic filter material. 10) Filter water level. 11) Filter floss (wool). 12) Sandbag weight. 13) Hose and tube attached securely with stainless steel clamp. 14) A thick, heavy lid, tightly fitted with no cracks.

While it is desirable to set up the tank in a place without a lot of pedestrian traffic, you do not want the fish to lack human contact entirely. Everyday viewing is necessary in order for the fish to gradually get used to having people around and should not be banned entirely in the process of avoiding vibration. The trick is simply to set up the tank with a foundation secure enough to absorb the shock that's incurred from a reasonable amount of observation.

The tank must have a lid, and it must be a sturdy one. *Polypterus* is an expert at escaping and leaping out of tanks. If you want to use a glass lid, use a thick one, not a thin piece that is easily broken. In that case the lid itself also acts like a weight as long as it fits neatly on the top of the tank. In contrast, if you choose to use an acrylic board as a lid you do not have to worry about it breaking, but you must remember to lay a weight on top of it to keep it in place. Also, baby fishes and *E. calabaricus* sometimes make their escape through holes that a heater or thermostat passes through, so you should make a point of plugging up any such openings.

It is best not to use underwater lighting. Not only can it cause injury when the fish surfaces for a breath of air, in the case of large specimens the light may get damaged as well. To provide for a breathing space, the water level should be no less than 2-3cm from the top of the tank.

THERMOSTATS AND WATER TEMPERATURE:

Considering the way these fish dash about when some bump or vibration gets them excited, it is not a good idea to use a glass tube-style thermostat when raising large-sized fishes. One option is to install it with the heater and thermometer inside the filter. With a transparent filter box, reading the numbers is not a problem, but it does tend to make confirming the regular workings of the heating apparatus troublesome. And if the tubing becomes undone or the pump breaks down, the heating equipment becomes ineffective.

So, what do you do about setting up equipment inside the tank? To prevent damage you must be careful. When raising large fishes, you are supposed to firmly secure the heating unit in place, but I have had at least two thermostats destroyed when set up that way. There used to be a heater guard on the market that could be attached to the tank wall with a suction cup, but this still led

110

to facial injuries, particularly to the sides of the mouth, most likely as the result of the fish getting caught in the space between the heater and cover. Then came the "willow branch idea," a method that implemented the bend-don't-break rubbery flexibility of a willow branch. You simply lean a waterproof thermostat against the tank wall at about a 45 degree angle. You do not have to secure it in place. To mitigate the impact if it is bounced around in the tank, just put some suction cups on it pointed toward the wall and lid. The heater should be covered and allowed to float freely without suction cups. This set-up has been accident-free so far, but I cannot recommend it to those who are more concerned with an esthetically pleasing layout.

Another new item is the battery-operated thermostat—a pretty effective device. The temperature readout part is small and attractive, and the whole unit is extremely durable. Recent models have the readout right on the mechanism box.

So, to sum up, the safest setup involves the battery-operated sensor and heater in the tank, and the heater covered and free-floating. Even for smaller species you can't go wrong doing it this way, particularly if you use a system in which the heater and thermostat are combined in one unit. With this kind of equipment it is important to be able to take care of problems immediately, so you should be sure to keep spare parts on hand. But remember, no matter how much spare equipment you have ready, it won't be of any help if you are not aware when something has gone wrong, so daily inspections are paramount.

Generally, when raising tropical fishes of any type it is best to keep the water temperature between 25-27°C. It is generally believed that they are well able to stand low temperatures, but since they do not necessarily like such conditions, you should try to avoid them. In midsummer, even if the temperature surpasses 30°C, as long as it is temporary it is no cause for alarm. In fact, their appetites tend to increase—so much so that overfeeding can become a health risk.

According to tank size, the type of filter and its particular problems will vary, so I have some examples for each tank size. When raising baby fish in the 30-36cm small-sized tank, Suisaku Eight free-floating filters and small, low-power underwater pumps are good to use. Maintenance is easy and you can get nearly airtight conditions with a lid, which means less chance of the fish escaping. You should also lightly spread some fine gravel on the bottom, and mix in coral and silica sand (in volume about one-third of the gravel) to prevent sudden changes in pH levels.

For a 45-60cm tank there are good pump/filter sets on the market. However, the problem with these outfits is that the hose gets knocked loose and makes a mess by spilling water outside the tank, so you have to do something to secure it yourself. The same sort of products are available for a 90cm tank, so check them out. When the tank is over 90cm, a top filter is generally used, and, considering the amount of waste generated in the tank, one with a high-capacity pump and a large filter box (water reserve type) should be used. There is no such thing as filtering too much. If you are keeping your *Polypterus* with other species that rely entirely on their gills for respiration, that is, they are not air breathers, you must remember to use an aerator just in case the hose should come loose. You should use a brand like Suisaku Eight, which will not come loose since it is attached with rubber bands and is basically a supplementary filter.

Other problem areas when setting up the equipment are the places where the pump and hose and hose and filter box connect. You can use stainless steel hose clamps and garbage bag ties for reinforcement. With more and more use, a rubber hose gradually starts to shrink because it is being pulled from both ends. It is a good idea to set the hose up with a bit of slack from the start and check it once in a while to see if it needs to be replaced. Since *Polypterus* species like to relax atop the hose, this is a particularly important point. Also, if you are raising small specimens that can fit inside the tube that drops down from the filter, be aware that these fish do sometimes manage to escape through it. This is not a problem if they only get as far as the filter box, but I have actually heard of several cases in which the fish managed to knock the lid off the filter box. A good plan is to put a fine meshed net over the top part of the tube. And, to be on the safe side, it is not a bad idea to put a weight on the lid of the filter box as well.

Recently, an assortment of new filter material has become available. You should try to find something that will not easily clog from the amount of waste your tank generates. As previously noted, a bit of large granule coral sand mixed in is extremely effective against sudden drops in pH. I use the following recipe, which should work well under most conditions, and I will describe it from the bottom layer up. First, you can put in some large grain coral sand, followed by "macaroni" ceramic material, then a layer of bioballs rising just above the water level, and finally a piece of wool on top.

As a general rule, the pH should be kept between 6.0-7.0, and though the fish can adapt to a fairly wide range as long as the changes are not sudden, the ideal range is slightly acidic to neutral. This will keep all the species stable in terms of appetite, body color, and behavior. In a test case in which the water was not changed and the pH dropped to a very acidic 4.0, the fish exhibited no change in appetite, but the body color became subdued and many of the specimens took to lying motionless at the bottom of the tank.

How often you need to change the water varies somewhat depending upon how many specimens you are raising. You can't go wrong, however, if you change one-third of the water once every one or two weeks and siphon away the debris on the bottom of the tank. Check the cleanliness of the filter box and clean it on a different schedule from the water change. You should not clean the filter and change the water at the same time.

FOOD AND FEEDING:

Polypterus species are mainly carnivores that feed on other fishes and crustaceans. Their eating habits do not change much from the hatchling stage to maturity. Whenever possible, it is best to provide them with a varied menu and bear in mind that rather than cut or portioned meat, they should be fed

the whole body. The following list of foods for each species is based on size.

WHITE WORMS: When you buy young fish they are usually about 10cm long and they can eat these to a certain extent, though they usually end up choking on them and throwing some up. Needless to say, this doesn't do much for the water quality.

BLOODWORMS: These are good for hatchlings of all species to small-sized types in their maturity. *Erpetoichthys calabaricus* is especially fond of bloodworms. Live, moving food is preferred, but once they get used to it, they will eat the frozen variety. The worms should be on the large size, and you can usually get them at a fishing store.

VARIOUS SPECIES OF SMALL FISHES: Generally, because they are so easy to obtain, goldfish are the most often used food of this type. However, feeder goldfish have been confirmed to contain Thiaminase (Vitamin B_1-destroying enzyme), so it is not very good to rely on them alone. The Loach, high in Vitamin B_1, is a good substitute. This is a fish that tends to swim about in the lower stratum, making it easier for the *Polypterus*, which usually hunt by waiting on the bottom for the food to pass by, to snag a meal. It is a particular favorite of *P. endlicheri*, which seems to pick up the scent and movement of this food fish as soon as it enters the tank. For small-sized specimens, including *E. calabaricus*, killifishes are a good choice. For *Polypterus*, be sure to throw in quite a large supply of fishes, like killifishes, that tend to swim in the middle and upper levels of the tank, which can be tough on their sluggish pursuer. The more feeder fishes, the higher the odds of a chance encounter. However, you cannot neglect proper maintenance and leave the remaining food in the tank to die; this is just asking for trouble in the form of deterioration of the water quality. Be sure to keep this in mind when dealing with large amounts of food.

CRUSTACEANS: Since *Polypterus* are hard-scaled fishes, you definitely want to provide them with a healthy, high-calcium crustacean diet. Depending upon the shop, you can find   shrimp sold specifically for use as feeders, but the quickest way is to collect them yourself. If you go to a river or pond at night and shine a flashlight, you are sure to find plenty of them. Scooping them up with a net is easy, and can even be a lot of fun. Just be sure to pay attention to where you are putting your feet down; working in the dark can be dangerous. For large-sized species, finger-length shrimp are desirable. You can collect these yourself too, though for the less industrious they are conveniently available at most food markets in the early morning. *Polypterus* also eat crawfish, though the bigger ones are often simply killed and not eaten, so it is important to use rather small ones.

Another favorite that is easy to obtain at food markets is frozen Muki shrimp. Since this type lacks a shell it isn't enough for a main diet, but does just fine as a side dish.

For small specimens you should cut up the food to an appropriate size. Having conducted a variety of tests on the subject, I have found that processed shrimp containing salt does not go over nearly so well as the saltless type. Whereas the former was practically ignored, the latter was nearly fought over. Further research is still being done on this matter.

Polypterus also enjoy a variety of krill that is on the market. In the beginning you will probably have to soak the krill in water and then let them sink to the bottom of the tank to make it easy for the *Polypterus* to get to them. But after a while they will come to the surface for them, which isn't bad exercise for the fish either.

Eventually, the size of the fish's belly should tell you how much to feed it. As a guideline for setting up a regular feeding schedule, feed them until the stomach swells slightly, then stop feeding for a day or two to allow for complete digestion.

When you have got more than one fish in the tank, whether they all are the same or different species of *Polypterus*, there is the possibility of overfeeding a bit in an attempt to make sure enough food gets to each individual specimen. If this does occur, simply extend the time interval between feedings a little more.

Trying to make the fish grow faster by repeatedly offering them food with a high fat content before they have had a chance to properly digest it can have dire consequences. Cases have been reported in which accumulation of fatty tissue in the stomach has led to the fish's death as a result of this sort of irresponsible raising.

COHABITATION:

Not only for the *Polypterus*, but for any carnivore with a territorial consciousness, the best way to prevent injury and stress is to simply keep them away from other fishes by raising each specimen alone. However, considering the great variety and unique characteristics of the different species of *Polypterus*, I can well understand the desire to increase the number of specimens in a tank. *Polypterus* is at least not as aggressive as the arowanas or cichlids, which pick fights with other fishes simply on sighting them from a distance. But if you've selected the right species and fulfill certain conditions, they are able to adjust relatively well to dwelling with other fishes.

First, to ease territorial instincts, there should be absolutely no layout or at least a minimal one. It is generally better to have several rather than one tank mate because then it is difficult to home in on one target of aggression (unless the fish is something like a Loach from a fish shop). The exact number depends on the species, size, and size of the tank, so I'll leave it up to your judgment. Of course, it is best not to raise only two specimens, since this most often leads to fights. This holds true for most carnivorous fishes. The sizes of the fishes should be about the same, even fish of the same species.

Besides taking the above precautions, whether you are raising your fish in a community situation from the beginning or introducing a *Polypterus* into an already inhabited tank somewhere along the line, you should make a point of carefully observing the tank, taking note of the extent of any fighting. To be on the safe side, it is also a good idea to have another tank ready, just in case the fish cannot get along at all. If you don't see any notable wounds on the fishes' bodies, there is a good chance that they will be able to get along. Although they generally settle into a very explicit power relationship (hierarchy) and behave somewhat violently, it doesn't necessarily mean they cannot cohabitate without killing one another. However, if the stronger fishes are determined to attack to the point of biting off fins, you will have to move either the stronger or the weaker fish to another tank.

In particular, it is best to avoid mixing *Polypterus* with the following species: Catfishes and snakeheads that are large enough to eat the *Polypterus*. In both these cases, however, the most important thing to consider is size compatibility. If size is pretty well balanced then, depending upon tank space, layout, and the number of specimens altogether, it might be possible.

Plecos (*Hypostomus* and their relatives) tend to menace *Polypterus* by sucking all over its skin. You may come across the two apparently living peacefully together in a shop, but it is wisest to avoid trying this at home. Also avoid fishes that, as a rule, are best raised by themselves, like *Protopterus*, piranhas, the Electric Eel and the Electric Catfish, both of which give off powerful electric shocks, Dorado, and *Gymnarchus*. Since all of these fishes are for the most part stubbornly persistent attackers, they are not good choices for cohabitation with *Polypterus*.

If you follow the fundamental guidelines explained above and work to establish a well-balanced community tank, you will find yourself pleasantly rewarded. You will be able to enjoy contrasting and comparing the various specimens, and chances are you will discover a new side of your fish's personality that only comes out when kept with others.

Polypterus can have their own personalities. For example, one might be a hearty eater and a bit fat, but easy-going and a poor fighter. Another fish may be too busy picking fights to take much interest in meal-time, and may make up for its slow-growing, small body with its aggressive nature and win more fights than it loses. Another specimen might be especially good at getting out of the way when bigger fishes like cichlids and arowanas cross its path. Then there's the cunning thief who steals food right out of other fish's mouths, thereby growing and rising up in the hierarchy.

In this way, you can see the

Happy tankmates. The fish on the left is a *Datnioides*.

aquarium as a microcosm of human society. The aquarist needs to be skilled in "personnel" in order to achieve a stimulating mix and bring out the best of the different fishes in the mixed tank.

SICKNESS AND INJURY:

First in the list of illnesses common to *Polypterus* is an illness related to parasites among those specimens imported into Japan. A type of freshwater leech, *Macrogyrodactylus polypteri*, attaches to the specimen's body and, using cells on the surface of the skin as its source of nutrition, breeds and multiplies. Initial symptoms include itchiness on the sides of the body. This causes the fish to seek relief by rubbing itself against something like the bottom sand or objects in the tank. As the parasites continue to multiply, you will notice what looks like hair seeming to grow on the infested fish's body. At this point the fish will begin to exhibit signs of "madness" like rotating its body and thrashing about violently. These are the final symptoms. If you don't do something at this point the fish will die. Such parasites are usually 2-3mm long, though 4-4.5mm is not unheard of. With careful observation they can be seen with the naked eye. If discovered, action should be taken without delay. For treatment, you should prepare a quarantine tank and add 250 ppm of formalin solution (formalin solution on the market diluted to ¼₀₀₀th strength) and then bathe the fish in the medicated water for 30 minutes. If the parasites are not exterminated the first time,

114

repeat the same process until they are. You should be particularly careful in the case of a mixed tank. In no time at all the parasites on a single infested fish can spread to other specimens, so it is a good idea to add some fish medicine to the regular tank too. Based on my own practical testing, half of the prescribed concentration of a product called Green F Gold is most effective.

Sometimes, if you are negligent about changing the water, healthy fishes may develop a milky condition in the eyeball. If left untreated, internal congestion and swelling can result in blindness. You can halt the process if you catch it early enough and immediately change the water. But if this isn't effective, you should apply some disinfectant (Malachite Green, Acriflavine, etc.) to the fish. However, because *Polypterus* are known to be rather sensitive to medicines, it is best to lower the dosage from about 1/2 to 2/3, depending on the severity of the symptoms.

If you are raising several specimens in one tank, injuries resulting from fights will be common, particularly partial loss of a fin. There is often little to worry about, however, since damage is usually confined to the soft, fleshy extension, which easily grows back. Likewise, violent altercations among larger specimens often lead to fractures of the spines of the dorsal fins. But as long as the basal part is not damaged, this, too, heals rather nicely by itself. However, because the specimen may have some difficulty catching food during the recuperation period, poor nutrition may cause the lost spine or fin part to grow back smaller than the original. You should keep this in mind and try to provide an appropriate variety and abundance of food to counteract the effect.

Facial attacks and the wounds that result are also frequent, but since there is little you can do to remedy the condition afterwards, taking preventive measures is the better option. Injuries to the side of the mouth (lips) generally heal completely back to normal, but more frontal injuries, always on the lower jaw, and the tearing of the lips of the upper jaw, probably will never return to their original condition. In this respect, you should pay particular attention to specimens that tend to play around a lot in the middle stratum of the tank, like *P. congicus*, *P. ornatipinnis*, *P. weeksii*, and so on.

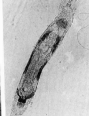

Left: *Polypterus* infested with *Macrogyrodactylus polypteri*, a parasitic condition. **Right:** Microscopic photograph of the parasite.

BREEDING *POLYPTERUS*

by Toshiaki Igarashi

The Polypteridae, found only in the fresh waters of Africa, figure prominently in the history of fish evolution, and are an extremely interesting group of primitive fishes. Two genera are extant, *Polypterus* and *Erpetoichthys*. The former, the type genus, consists of 10 species and 14-16 subspecies, and the latter, the sister genus, has only a single known species (Poll, 1941; Daget, 1954; Gosse, 1988, 1990).

In the past ten years, in Japan, there have been several instances of the captive breeding of *Polypterus* reported in aquarium magazines. Counting unverified cases, there are breeding reports of at least six species and seven subspecies, plus cases of cross-breeding.

SEX DIFFERENCES:

For starters, it is necessary to understand the differences between male and female

Sex differences in the anal fin of *Polypterus senegalus* (female above, male below). Generally there is a very distinct space between the anal and caudal fins, but in the White Nile specimens described by Boulenger the space is filled in by several thin spines that look like a second anal fin. In explaining this, he points out that the caudal fin has a tendency to be asymmetrical, and of all the species he has encountered, this tendency is most common in *P. senegalus* (Boulenger, 1907).

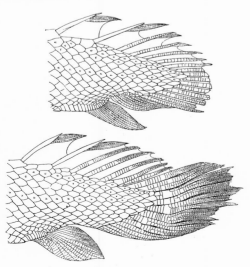

Polypterus. It is known that the female tends to be larger than the male (Harrington, 1898; Daget et al., 1965). Another index for sex determination, in *Erpetoichthys* as well, is the shape of the anal fin. There are several studies concerned with sex difference evident in the anal fin. For example Boulenger (1907), of the British Museum, found that the male's anal fin is wider than that of the female. Furthermore, the spines of the anterior dorsal fins are thicker in males, and the ribbed base is bigger (see fig. 1).

Besides these external differences, there is an internal difference (fig. 2). In the caudal skeleton of the male, the support of the forward section of the anal fin is made up of only one bone that fans into three sections.

Recently, in a study at the Tokyo Agricultural University (Yamanaka, et al., 1989), an SEM (scanning electron microscope) was used to examine the scale structure of the two genera, and a clear sex difference was found in the surface protrusions of the scales. The surfaces of the scales of the male protrude more, and it is said that the difference can be detected by touch.

EXAMPLES OF CAPTIVE BREEDING FROM THE LITERATURE (FROM THE PAPERS OF ARNOULT):

As I mentioned above, there have been many reports of successful captive breeding of *Polypterus* in Japan recently, but when we actually look into them, we find that most were rather dependent on luck, and few were based on an understanding of the natural habitat or behavior of the species. Furthermore, as far as I can tell, there has been no evidence of any essential development of spawning methods.

I am slowly moving toward the establishment of methods for inducing spawning, but for reasons of research it is difficult to publish any findings at this

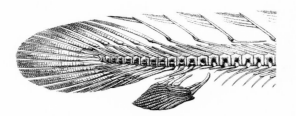

The caudal skeleton of a male *Polypterus senegalus* (adapted from Boulenger, 1907).

time. Furthermore, as understandable as the desire is for less moderate importation of the fish, I do not want to see more aimless "keeping" of this fish; more specimens for breeding is a slightly different story.

First, then, I have especially selected several research papers from the accumulated scholarly literature. These are papers by a scientist named Arnoult, of the Paris Museum of Natural History, who vigorously studied and published on the problem of breeding *Polypterus* from the viewpoints of generative biology and husbandry in the early 1960's. I believe that this research is entirely unknown in the Japanese tropical fish world, especially the 1964 paper entitled "Comportement et reproduction en captivité de *Polypterus senegalus* Cuvier," the crowning achievement of his research. Using specimens gathered in Burkina Faso, the reproduction of two generations is reported in great detail. This research is the first instance of *Polypterus* reproduction and raising of a new generation in an aquarium. His methods are similar in spots to mine, and his results will certainly serve as a fine reference for aspiring breeders, so I now quote the paper almost in its entirety.

"Comportement et reproduction en captivité de *Polypterus senegalus*," by Jacques Arnoult (Ichthyological Research Lab, National Museum of Natural History, Paris).

"The raising of *Polypterus* has become much more common since the 50's. In fact, one can find most species in the large public aquariums. At the same time, many labs are working on breeding and raising this fish in the hope of making complete the extremely fragmentary knowledge we have of its reproduction and early development.

Polypterus is hardy and lives a long time in the aquarium. However, on March 15, 1962, I was thrilled to see eggs in the laboratory tank of *P. senegalus* and I set about making notes on this discovery; the eggs had not yet hatched. I have made two preliminary reports on my biological observations of this fish and the eggs themselves, and I will just repeat the basics here.

Of all species of *Polypterus*, *P. senegalus* has the widest range, and it is generally found in the rivers and swamps of Upper Volta (name changed to Burkina Faso in

Nymphaea lotus (Tiger Lotus).

1984). The pair that first spawned on March 15, 1963, are two of nine young that I collected with a hand net in November, 1959, in a flood plain in Upper Volta that was rich with aquatic plants (*Nymphaea lotus*, *Ceratophyllum demersum*). These young *Polypterus* had clear external gills, and were less than 10cm long. A few days later I put them in plastic bags and flew back to France.

In Paris, I placed these in a one meter square, 35cm deep tank. The water was close in composition to the fresh water of the waterways of Upper Volta.

I. CHEMICAL CHARACTERISTICS OF UPPER VOLTA WATER

1. Temperature: Although water temperature is more stable than air temperature, it does go through radical changes over the

117

temperatures are 30°C in May-June and 22°C in January, and the average low temperatures are 29°C in June-July and 20°C in January. The water temperature also fluctuates over the course of the day, but the range is quite small, especially in rivers and deep marshes. On the other hand, the temperature in certain very shallow swamps rises so much in a day that it is hard to believe that any fish can live in it. In these hot baths, *Clarias* and sometimes *Polypterus* species are found.

2. Muddiness: Like all the waters of the West African savannah, the waters of Upper Volta are never very clear. The extremely fine muddy sediment never settles.

3. pH: We usually found a pH level that fluctuated between 6.0 and 7.0. During the dry season, the pH remained fairly consistently just above 6.0. Then, suddenly, with the first rains in June, the water clearly becomes alkaline and the pH level takes off. The alkalinity varies through the time of heaviest precipitation in August and September, and then it begins to fall.

4. Hardness: The waters of Upper Volta usually have very little salts of calcium or magnesium, but the hardness does depend on the season. As in Europe, when rainwater flows along the ground the calcium salt content increases, and this affects the hardness of the surface water to a certain extent. But the earth in Upper Volta is actually poor in soluble materials, and rain contains only a small amount of mineral salts, so, if anything, the hardness of the water actually decreases during the rains. Generally speaking, the level never exceeds 5 in the dry season, and it will fall as low as 0 during rainy season.

5. Alkalinity: The alkali reserve (carbonic and bicarbonate salts) that can be measured in SBV is small, and it varies with the water's hardness. In the rainy month of August, the SBV is at 0.35, and reaches 0.475 at the height of the dry season.

Male *Polypterus senegalus* courting a female.

II. THE BEHAVIOR OF *P. SENEGALUS* IN CAPTIVITY

The young *Polypterus* brought back from Upper Volta were placed in a large, solid tank with a sand substrate, and the water hardness was 3-4 from the start. The water was heavily aerated but not filtered, and the temperature was kept at 25°C. These young were provided with a nutritionally rich diet based on chironomid larvae, but their growth was still very slow in the winter months. Other foods tried with them were earthworms, tubificid worms, water fleas, and young guppies, but none were eaten. This supported the literature that indicated that *Polypterus* was not much of a fearsome carnivore. The fish is extremely cautious about food, and in the wild only rarely eats other fishes.

This fish does not like light, and would only come to the surface at the spot where the footlight shines, as it would rise to the sunny surface of the water in its native Africa. It spent most of its time resting near the bottom, its dorsal fins waving slightly back and forth like fans. When it moved about slowly, it needed only to use its dorsal fins, or it would use the rear of its body to propel itself.

Polypterus rises to the surface of the tank to breathe oxygen from the air, but the intervals between such respirations are extremely irregular. Therefore, this must be only a secondary method of respiration, and not necessary for survival as it is in *Protopterus*.

The degeneration of the external gills had not begun in September, 1960, and was still not complete in December.

In February, 1961, I recognized

some slight changes in body size and appearance in these nine experimental specimens, and I was able to determine the sex characteristics from sight and isolate three pairs. As described in the literature, the anal fin of the male was much thicker and longer than that of the female, and the base of the tail swelled horizontally. The female could be identified by the largeness of the whole rear half of her body.

I prepared special water for the breeding tanks. This water was a mix of one part water from a marsh in Senaar forest to three parts double-changed water. This marsh water was slightly acidic with a hardness of 3 and a pH of 6.0. The tannin content was very high, indicating dissolved oak leaves. In the new medium with hardness 4, pH 6.3, the fish would suddenly behave erratically. Rather than relaxing together near the bottom, the pairs would open and shut their mouths over and over while continually changing the direction they faced. The male liked to swim along the left side of the female and frequently attempt to bite her head, or he would curl himself along the groove in her torso and simulate sexual contact. Even after such promising behavior there was no evidence of spawning, but with some help from gonadotropin, I was able to induce spawning in one exceptional pair. Unfortunately, the eggs did not reach the point of hatching.

In the beginning of 1962, I tried it again under similar conditions. I added 0.5g of seawater per liter of water, stopped bottom filtering, and merely aerated the water with an air compressor. I didn't use hormones with any of the fish, but the same pair that had produced the unfertilized eggs spawned again on March 15, 1962, this time normally. Most hatched, and 62 young of different stages of development were born. Twenty of them survived to sexual maturity, so I was able to make several pairs of fully developed fish within a year, in February of 1963.

The water of these breeding tanks was the same as that used in March of 1962 for the previous generation. Within three to four months, all the pairs began displaying the sort of mating behavior described above. One female laid eggs on April 25 that did not develop normally, but the same pair successfully spawned on May 24, and then another pair followed on the 26th. Then on May 30 and 31 two more pairs spawned, and then an older first generation pair spawned again.

The interesting thing about the reproduction by the second generation (F_2) is that it was not random, but it showed that tank breeding of *Polypterus* is possible as long as the biological and chemical conditions are sufficiently met. Furthermore, I believe that adding the seawater provided trace elements that had some special effect.

Stages of development of *Polypterus senegalus* (Kerr, 1907).

119

III. EGGS AND YOUNG

P. senegalus eggs are spherical and small, about 0.9mm, and enveloped in a gelatinous substance. The transparent animal pole is in the center of a zone with a lot of melanin, and the opposite pole, the vegetal pole, has spots. The female lays the eggs on a plant in the water that she slightly contacts. I placed some coconut fiber that I had previously boiled for securing the eggs in the tank, and the next year I used nylon strands. *Polypterus* like these materials and prefer to lay their eggs on them.

Whether the eggs are removed by taking out the object they are attached to or one by one with a pipette, it is important to remove them as soon as possible. They should be put in a small tank with a filter system. They develop very quickly at a temperature of 28°C. Hatching is completed in 60 hours, and the newly-hatched young resemble tadpoles.

They usually lie on their bellies but are capable of some movement. They have small external gills which they use for respiration.

About 12 hours after hatching, their appearance changes. They become rounder in the head and body, and the tail becomes longer. The eyes and pectoral fins become distinguishable, and the external gills become comb-like. The mouth is not fully formed but its location is clear, and two organs under the eyes become noticeable.

Within another 8 hours, the eyes and mouth become functional and the young fish begin searching for their own food. The total length at this point is about 4mm. The fry is not able to pick out food and pursue it; it only eats what happens to pass right before its mouth, so this is a crucial stage. My first attempts at feeding were failures. All the young died of starvation right beside the infusoria (Tekichuu) and tiny bits of plants that I tried to feed them. After that I used nothing but newly hatched brine shrimp, and in such large numbers that the young had no trouble finding and eating them.

Top: Young *Polypterus delhezi*, 5 cm long. **Center:** Young *Polypterus palmas*, 6 cm long. **Bottom:** Willow Moss.

Another advantage of this food is that tiny crustaceans do not dirty the water as much as other foods when they die, an important consideration because the young *Polypterus* are sensitive to dirty water the first days of their life.

After 15 days the young fish no longer look like tadpoles and begin to vigorously prey on the crustaceans swimming nearby. They still differ from adult fish in that the dorsal is continuous and they have fibrous external gills. They will mature quickly now as long as they get enough nutrition. They are yellow with vivid black bands. In about a month they will develop small fins and the dorsal will break up into separate parts.

In 1963, through this breeding effort, I was able to observe the growth, as well as clearly determine the sizes and weights of 116 specimens. I kept only 20 in

120

order to plot a maturation curve, and now, in February, 1964, 17 still remain."

THE BASIC FACTS OF BREEDING AND A SUMMARY

Now, following Arnoult's research, I would like to add some supplementary information using *P. senegalus* as an example.

The courting male has been observed bumping the female's body with his head at first, but he gradually becomes more interested in chasing after her tail. The frequency of this behavior increases as the days go on, until at last the pair selects a plant with narrow leaves and spawns. At that time, as soon as the female finds a spot by digging around with her nose, she prepares to spawn by assuming a set position, either straight or turned over, and the male follows suit as he comes up beside her. The male uses his anal fin to repeatedly stimulate the area around the female's ovipositor. Now the female deposits from five to ten eggs and the male fertilizes them. For one or two days they go back and forth from tail-chasing to spawning in cycles, so that in the end 100-300 adhesive eggs are laid. These will hatch in another three days. The parents should be separated from the eggs immediately since they might eat them.

The breeding tank can never be too large, but for a pair of about 25cm each a standard 60cm tank should be sufficient, even if they do seem a little cramped. As a matter of fact, I have a pair of *P. palmas* of 25cm that spawned in a 45cm tank. As for the setup, power filters could be dangerous by sucking up eggs and newly-hatched fry, and bottom filters are hard to maintain, so a sponge filter is best. The author uses two sponge filters, one on each side, in a 60cm tank.

Water temperatures between 24°C and 28°C, and a pH from 4.8 to 7.5 are the working ranges for this brief period. But it isn't difficult to keep the pH in the 6.0-6.5 range, and this will get more positive results. If you use methylene blue or other chemicals

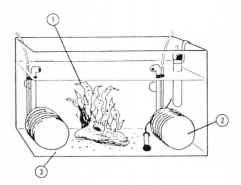

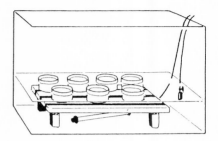

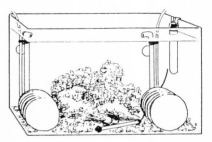

Top: 1) Plant with eggs transferred *as is*. **2)** Sponge filters. **3)** No bottom gravel. **Center:** Hatching and young set-up. Separate cups for each youngster. **Bottom:** The Willow Moss provides many hiding places.

for fungus, use it sparingly because high concentrations can cause deformities.

For the sake of maintenance and feeding, bottom gravel should not be used. After hatching, the young live off their yolk sac for six to seven days, at which point feeding should begin. Baby brine shrimp (nauplii) are suitable, but it is important to adjust the filter current so that the food will not be made to sink in hard-to-get-at places. Seven to ten days after feeding begins, the mortality rate increases due to fights. Under ideal circumstances, from this time until several weeks later, when they reach about 2-3cm, each individual would be raised separately in cups in wide, shallow tanks like the one in the diagram. If that is impossible, they could be kept in tanks with a large amount of Willow Moss for hiding. After they exceed 2cm, they can be fed tubificid worms, and they become much more active. Once they reach about 4cm, then they are in safer waters. They will most likely survive, and they start to resemble the *Polypterus* we all know.

ACKNOWLEDGEMENTS:

I would like to express my thanks to all those who helped me complete this paper, especially Hiroshi Higashi of the Tropical Fish Research Center for his information about captive breeding; Kiyoshi Suzuki of Tokyo Agricultural University for his information about sex differences; and Kaoru Komakata of Tokyo Agricultural University.

BIBLIOGRAPHY:

Arnoult, J. 1961. Premiéres observations en captivité sur poissons de la famille des Polypteridae: *Polypterus senegalus senegalus* Cuvier. Comportement sexuel et ponte provoquée. *Bull. Mus. nat. Hist. Nat., Paris*, (2)33(4):391-395, 1 fig.

Arnoult, J. 1962. Ponte naturelle suivie d'eclosions chez *Polypterus senegalus* Cuvier. *C. r. hebd. Séanc. Acad., Paris*, 254(15):2828-2829.

Arnoult, J. 1964. Comportement et reproduction en captivité de *Polypterus senegalus* Cuvier. *Acta Zool. Stockholm*, 46:191-199, 3 figs.

Boulenger, G. A. 1907. *Zoology of Egypt. The Fishes of the Nile.* 2 vols., London, 578pp., pls. A-F, i-xcvii.

Daget, J. 1954. Les poissons du Niger supérieur. *Mém. I.F.A.N.*, 36:391pp., 141 figs.

Daget, J., M.l. Bouchot, & J. Arnoult. 1965. Etude de la croissance chez *Polypterus senegalus* Cuvier. *Acta Zool., Stockholm*, 46(3):297-309, 4 figs.

Gosse, J.-P. 1988. Révision systématique de deux espéces du genre *Polypterus* (Pisces, Polypteridae). *Cybium* 12(3):239-245, 1 fig.

Gosse, J.-P. 1990. Polypteridae: *in* C. Lévéque, D. Paugy, & G. G. Teugels, ed. Faune des poissons d'eaux douces et saumatres de l'Afrique de l'Ouest. *Faune Tropicale, Tome 1, ORSTOM & MRAC*, 28:79-87, 8 figs.

Harrington, N. R. 1898. The life habits of *Polypterus*. *Amer. Nat.*, 33:721-728.

Kerr, J.G. 1907. The development of *Polypterus senegalus* Cuv.: *in* J. G. Kerr, ed. *The Budgett Memorial Volume, Cambridge University Press*, 195-284, 67 figs, 3 pls.

Poll, M. 1941. Contribution á l'etude systématique des Polypteridae (Pisc.). *Rev. Zool. Bot. Afr.*, 35(2):141-179, 12 figs.

Yamanaka, K., K. Suzuki, M. Oki, 1989. *The Sexual Types of Polypteridae.* The Annual Meeting of the Japan Ichthyology Assoc.: Paper Summaries, p.9.

RAISING STURGEON

by the Editors

Famous for their roe, better known as caviar, the sturgeons, the common name for species of this order, are classified in class Osteichthys, subclass Actinopterygii, superorder Chondrostei, and order Acipenseriformes. In Japan, it is often the common name for the species *Acipenser medirostis*. The sturgeon is thought to be a descendant of the palaeoniscids, which lived in the Silurian and Devonian periods at the height of the Paleozoic Era some 350 million years ago. The family Chondrosteidae, closely related to today's sturgeons, appeared in the Jurassic period about 150 million years ago. One well-known fossil member of the family is *Chondrosteus*. The sturgeons come on the scene in the later Cretaceous period.

The taxonomy of the modern sturgeon is not at all settled; there are a number of difficult cases of species of Acipenseridae that have not been convincingly classified, i.e., some species may be mistakenly treated as two species, etc. Having said that, let us move on.

The genus *Huso*, of the sturgeon family Acipenseridae and including two species, can nowadays be seen only in aquariums. Genus *Acipenser*, comprised of some 20 species, includes the main sturgeons imported as ornamental fishes. However, there are two species of shovel-nosed sturgeons, genus *Scaphirhynchus*, and three of *Pseudoscaphirhyncus* imported now as well.

The family Polyodontidae has two genera and two species that are extant, *Polyodon spathula* of North America and *Psephurus gladius* of China. These two species are considered to differ from the sturgeons at the subordinal level (suborder Polyodontoidei).

Since they prefer the cold waters north of the temperate zone, they are found in northern Eurasia, Canada,

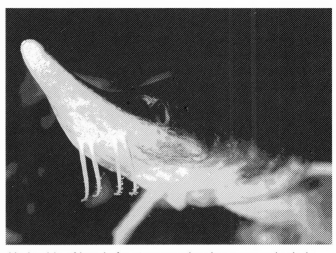

Underside of head of a sturgeon showing sensory barbels.

and the northern U.S., we cannot call the sturgeons tropical fishes. Four or five species have been recorded as caught off the coast of Japan, and it is said that sturgeons have spawned in the rivers of Hokkaido and Tohoku, but such things have certainly not happened at all in recent years.

Morphology and Habitat:

The Japanese name for sturgeon is "chozame," or "butterfly shark." It is explained in the literature that this name comes from the five rows of diamond-shaped plates that look like hinges (*chotsugai*, "butterfly pairs"). Of course it should be added that they are not members of the shark family.

Though there have been reports of White Sturgeons feeding on young seals, sturgeons generally feed on plankton and other invertebrates. Their ventral mouths are useful for feeding on bottom-dwelling animals, and sturgeons constantly scan the bottom for shellfish, crustaceans, lugworms, insect larvae, and fish eggs. Sometimes small fishes are eaten.

Sturgeons usually live in the ocean but head to inland rivers to spawn, after which they return to the sea again. They will also leave the ocean in extremely cold weather in order to wait out the winter in a deep hole in the bottom of a body of fresh water. They prefer the mouths of rivers and shallow straits, which are usually rich in the life they like to feed on. Though sturgeons move in and out of fresh water often, no known species exclusively inhabit fresh water.

Sturgeons take a long time to mature and live to an old age. The Little Sturgeon (*Acipenser ruthenus*) lives to around 20 years, but a White Sturgeon that lived to an age of 82 is recorded in the *Guinness Book of World Records*. It has been claimed that the Russian Sturgeon, *A. gueldestadti*, lives to 100-120 years of age. Despite that, the clumsy sturgeon is certainly one of the most primitive fishes in this book of primitives, perhaps matched in crudeness only by *Neoceratodus*.

CARE:

1. Acquisition.–International trade of some species of sturgeons and paddlefishes is restricted under the CITES treaty. At the time of this writing (July, 1992), four species are listed in Appendices I and II of CITES: *Acipenser brevirostrum, A. sturio, A. oxyrhynchus,* and *Polyodon spathula*. However, many species of sturgeon and paddlefish are bred in hatcheries for their roe, and these of course do not deplete the wild populations. *P. spathula* is raised along with Longnose Gar in northern Germany, and the young we get are imported not from their native North America but from Europe. Such specimens obviously can be traded.

Breeders are widely engaged in cross-breeding sturgeons in order to increase their strengths. For example, they have successfully created a hybrid of the Great Siberian Sturgeon and the Little Sturgeon that combines the fast growth of the former with the tolerance of high temperatures of the latter. When a hybrid like this is imported for display without an accompanying explanation, it becomes very hard to determine just what it is. A certain "Blunt-nosed Sturgeon" we imported once is thought to be the result of this kind of cross-breeding.

The specimens that are imported

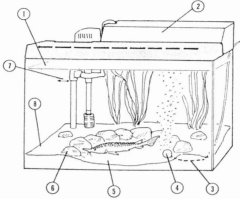

1) Tank should be as large as possible. Cylindrical tanks are okay. 2) Use both a top and a bottom filter. 3) Bury the tube under the sand. 4) Airstone. 5) Vary the sand level. 6) Arrange rocks so that fish cannot get its head stuck. 7) Make sure spaces between tubes and glass are enough so that fishes cannot get stuck. 8) Coral or Kei sand.

are generally young but as large as possible, since it is usually summer and they must be able to take the heat. Choose one that swims around energetically seeking food, and avoid those that display any unusual swimming style.

2. Tank and Set-up.–The sturgeon is a big fish that likes to flex its fins—give it room. The bigger the tank the better. Going by size, any specimen over 10cm needs a 60cm tank; over 30cm, a 90cm tank is needed. Area is more important than depth, and it is best not to put in much driftwood or stone. For the substrate, beach sand or fine coral sand is best. The young do not need

The Chinese Paddlefish can reportedly reach lengths of 7 meters. It feeds on fishes and crabs (from *Chinese Freshwater Fish Atlas*).

any salt water, but when they exceed 20cm at the latest, change from a fourth to a third of the water to salt water. The filter should be a top filter with coral sand or charcoal for filtering material. The current should be on the strong side. Aeration to increase the oxygen content must not be neglected.

3. Maintenance.–The temperature should be kept at 15-20°C. Sturgeons will die from temperatures over 30°C. Of course, keeping the water cool, both technically and economically no easy task, is the hardest part of keeping sturgeons. A heater does the trick in the winter, but to get the sturgeons through the hot summer a tank cooler is ideal. If that method is unfeasible, the tank should be located in an air-conditioned room or at least a cool, breezy place. When it is warm, the amount of water per fish should be increased, aeration should be turned up, water changes should be more frequent, and so on. Without these measures, survival of the sturgeon is unlikely.

4. Feeding.–In general, sturgeons are big eaters. They should get a varied diet of brine shrimp, daphnia, earthworms, bloodworms, lugworms, small fishes, and pieces of fish. Two feedings a day or more are recommended, especially when they are young. They can get used to bottom pellets. Frequent feedings mean dirty water, and the successful aquarist aims for clean water at all times, so a third of the water should be changed on a regular schedule.

Lungfish poking its head out from plants.

RAISING LUNGFISHES

by Toshiaki Igarashi

Recently there has been much debate over the original relationships between, on the one hand, lungfishes and Crossopterygians, of which the Coelacanth is the most famous example, and, on the other, land vertebrates. Even if they have no particular interest in such questions, most people have heard of lungfishes. They encounter them in textbooks, encyclopedias, and aquariums, and the impression made by the "living fossil" that illustrates a great step in vertebrate evolution remains with them a long time.

TAXONOMY:

At present, lungfishes comprise two orders, Ceratodontiformes and Lepidosireniformes, which are subdivided into three families, three genera, six species and nine subspecies. In the order Ceratodontiformes there is only the family Ceratodontidae, which contains the single genus and species *Neoceratodus forsteri* (Krefft, 1870) of Australia. In the Lepidosireniformes are the families Lepidosirenidae, also with a single genus and species, *Lepidosiren paradoxa* (Fitzinger, 1837) of South America, and the Protopteridae, in which are included the remaining genus and four species, *Protopterus annectens* (Owen, 1839), *P. aethiopicus* (Heckel, 1851), *P. amphibius* (Peters, 1844), and *P. dolloi* (Boulenger, 1900), all from Africa.

The first two species of *Protopterus* have subspecies, but they are rarely mentioned in the literature, at least in what is available in Japan. I will briefly explain the differences between the species and subspecies here since these are important for taxonomy. These revisions, carried out by Poll (1961) of the Belgian Royal Central African Museum, we include below with the original recordings of the subspecies, and the descriptions from Boulenger's *Catalogue of the Fresh-Water Fishes of Africa* (1909). In addition, Gosse's taxonomy and bibliography on body length, and the largest known lengths today are appended below.

The following values are listed below: (1) ratio of the distance from the tip of the snout to the origin of the anal fin to the total length of the body; (2) ratio of the length of the head to the distance from the tip of the snout to the origin of the anal fin; (3) the ratio of the distance from the tip of the snout to the origin of the dorsal fin to the distance from the tip of the snout to the origin of the anal fin; (4) the ratio of the length of the pectoral fin to the distance from the tip of the snout to the origin of the anal fin; (5) the ratio of the length of the pelvic fin to the distance from the tip of the snout to the origin of the anal fin; (6) the number of ribs; (7) the number of scales in a line from the origin of the anal fin forward. Numbers (1)-(5) and (7) are averages, and those figures that have a range mainly express recognized variations arising from geographical differences among the specimens from a single subspecies.

Protopterus annectens:

P. a. annectens (Owen, 1839). Specimens from West Africa: (1) 54.2% (2) 28.4% (3) 57.5% (4) 51% (5) 35.5% (6) 34-37 (7) 50. Total lengths 82cm and up.

P. a. brieni (Poll, 1961). Specimens from Katanga or Zambezi Rivers: (1) 52.3-53% (2) 23.7-25% (3) 51-51% (4) 42.5-45% (5) 32.1-39.8% (6) 32-35 (7) 48-49. Total lengths 60.1cm and up.

P. aethiopicus:

P. ae. aethiopicus (Heckel, 1851). Specimens from Lakes Edward or Tanganyika: (1) 53.7-58% (2) 24.8-27.4% (3) 63.5-65.4% (4) 48.4-78.7%

Protopterus aethiopicus aethiopicus.

(5) 48.7-51.6% (6) 37-38 (7) 62. Total lengths 2m.

P. ae. congicus (Poll, 1961). Specimens from Katanga or Stanley Pool (albinos included): (1) 54.4-58% (2) 22.1-25% (3) 62.1-64.5% (4) 51.6-53.6% (5) 40.6-54.5% (6) 37-41 (Katanga), 38-39 (Stanley Pool) (7) 60-61. Total lengths 1m and up.

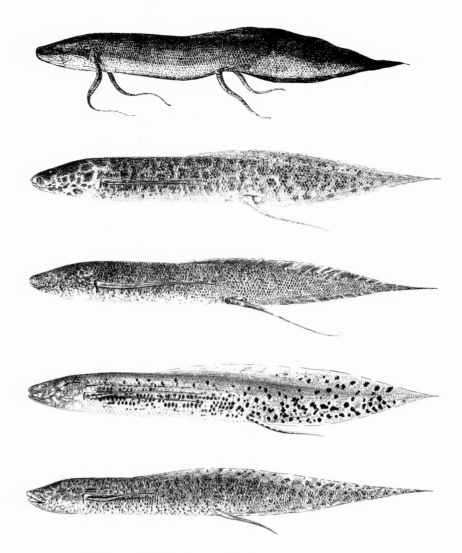

From top to bottom: *Protopterus aethiopicus aethiopicus* (Boulenger 1907, 1909). *Protopterus aethiopicus congicus* (Poll, 1961). Protopterus aethiopicus mesmaekersi (Poll, 1961). *Protopterus annectens annectens* (Poll, 1961). *Protopterus annectens brieni* (Poll, 1961).

P. ae. mesmaekersi (Poll, 1961). Specimens from the Congo basin: (1) 52.5-58% (2) 25.3% (3) 67.1% (4) 68.8% (5) 55.8% (6) 38-40 (7) 59. Total lengths 95.3cm and up.

BEHAVIOR:

Here I will discuss mainly the genus *Protopterus*, relying on the work of Greenwood (1986) and Banister (1987), both of the British Museum, as well as that of Poll (1961) cited above.

The most important characteristic of the lungfishes is obvious from their common name: the swim bladder has become specialized to the point of functioning as lungs. This development is particularly remarkable in the South American genus *Lepidosiren* and the African genus *Protopterus*, whose swim bladders have become

126

Young specimens are usually more colorful than the adults and are welcomed as aquarium pets.

compartmentalized into two lungs, one on each side, which are structurally similar to those of land vertebrates. They are highly dependent on aerial respiration, and their gills have become correspondingly degenerated. In comparison, the swim bladder of the Australian genus *Neoceratodus* is only partially divided into two compartments, and it relies on its gills about as much as any other fish.

The former two genera are already well-known for their summer hibernation behavior, which makes use of the functioning lungs. They are distributed in areas characterized by wet and dry seasons, where in the dry seasons most bodies of water dry up. As the water dries up, the lungfish buries itself in the bottom mud with its body bent in half and its head pointing up. It secretes a mucus that acts as a cocoon to keep its body moist, and it leaves a small air hole for breathing. It remains this way for several months until the rains return. This hibernation has been reported for three species of *Protopterus*. *Lepidosiren* differs slightly; apparently it doesn't create a mucous cocoon.

What sorts of habitats do these lungfishes live in? They seem to generally prefer shallow water systems; at least this has been confirmed with all species of *Protopterus*. However, *P. aethiopicus* has been spotted in fairly far offshore parts of Lake Victoria in water over 20m deep, and it has been taken in drag nets in waters over 30m deep as well. It is not known for sure if it is distributed in other large lakes, but *P. aethiopicus* is a regular feature of the life found in the shallows of lakes such as Lake Victoria, in the

surrounding grassy swamps, and water lily and papyrus marshes. Schools of *Protopterus* are found in seasonally flooded marshes and the edges of slow flowing rivers, and more rarely in fast current rivers.

Observations in both the wild and in the laboratory have led researchers to believe that *Protopterus* determines the location of its food with its sense of smell, which is supplemented by the taste buds found on the pectoral fins. The basis for attributing the location of food to the sense of smell is not clear, but from investigations on the systematics of *P. annectens* it has been found that a large number of taste buds are spread around its pectoral fins and the skin over its pelvics, and the final opinion is that their nerve cells are of the same type as those in taste buds found in the mouth.

When it feeds, it first regurgitates then slowly and thoroughly chews its food. It can gulp prey quickly, though, thanks to its large *recticervis* muscle which moves its tongue cartilage, giving it powerful sucking power. From the records of the contents of the intestines of captured specimens, we can safely say that at least mature *P. annectens* and *P. aethiopicus* are omnivorous carnivores. They eat a wide range of prey, including crustaceans, insect larvae, and other invertebrates, but most commonly mollusks. They do not eat vertebrates much. However, reports indicate that directly after awakening from the summer hibernation, the large *P. annectens* eat the smaller ones. Plant matter has also been found in the intestines, but whether it was taken as food or just by chance is not known.

Next I will briefly describe my observations of lungfish reproduction:

Sometime around August, *Neoceratodus* spawns by scattering its eggs in a small area of a plant-filled shallow.

Of the *Protopterus* species, little is known about *P. amphibius*, but the other three species spawn during the rainy season. For example, *P. aethiopicus* spawns in the northern part of Lake Victoria between November and April, and reproduction peaks in the first and last two months of that period. They will spawn during unseasonal rains, too, if they are heavy enough. Catch records in the area over a period of 22 months showed females to be more commonly caught than males by a ratio of 96:29. There were many immature females among these and the surrounding marshes and waters over 10m deep were not sampled, so this sex ratio should not be taken as the natural one. It may give an idea of where the non-reproductive population prefers to gather, though. All three species build spawning nests in plant-filled areas near the banks, and the male stays around the nest to guard the hatchlings.

Lepidosiren also builds nests for spawning. Again, the male protects the hatchlings, but in this genus the species develops unusual thread-like protrusions on its pectoral fins. It is not known for certain, but they are believed to be supplemental respiratory organs for this stressful protection period.

Acquisition:

Lungfishes have been kept in aquariums, of course, and by hobbyists in aquaria for a relatively long time in Japan. As early as 1968, *P. aethiopicus* graced the cover of an aquarium magazine. At present, all species of South American *Lepidosiren* and African *Protopterus* can be bought in stores. International trade of the Australian *Neoceratodus* is extremely restricted by the Washington Accord, and, before that, protection by the Australian government made raising it out of the question.

It should be noted that due to recently begun captive breeding overseas, young *P. dolloi* should be becoming especially inexpensive. This is a welcome development in that it will encourage artificial breeding of species on which this has never been attempted, thereby furthering our understanding of the biology of wild specimens.

BASIC DIFFERENCES IN RAISING THE DIFFERENT GENERA:

Lepidosiren and *Protopterus* differ in the fundamental area of combined raising. *Lepidosiren* are mild-tempered, so as long as there is no great difference in size, they can be raised with same-species specimens, or a different species if it is compatible with *Lepidosiren*'s

nocturnal habits.

On the other hand, *Protopterus* is fiercely territorial and combative, so all species should be raised individually. Occasionally, fish shops will have a tank with a number of young together, but this practice should not be tried at home. At first there may not seem to be any problems, but the biting will start and quickly become dangerous. Any fin can be targeted, but tail fins are most often bitten, and bite-sized missing chunks are not uncommon. These will grow back, but there is no guarantee they will grow to the original size or color. I personally know of an incident resulting from mixing species. Pirarucu (*Arapaima gigas*) and several other species were put in with *P. amphibius* in a fairly uncrowded tank. After about a month, when everything appeared to be going smoothly, the aquarist checked the tank in the morning to find the Pirarucu floating dead, its belly ripped open. The wound was clearly inflicted by the *P. amphibius*. He had been feeding and watching them carefully—there was no warning whatsoever. And the two fish were about the same length.

SET-UP:

The Tank.–Among the lungfishes that are imported into Japan is the largest extant species, *P. aethiopicus*. This designation is actually based on records of *P. ae. aethiopicus*, but the origins of the shipments suggest the possibility that it is one of the other subspecies that is imported. There are records of a total length of 2 meters for *P. ae. aethiopicus*, but even the smallest species, *P. amphibius*, grows to total lengths of 60cm. It is not impossible to limit growth somewhat, but one wants to do it as naturally as possible, especially when it is a big species, for the fish's as well as the keeper's sake. Therefore, a minimum tank size of 90-180cm is recommended. However, it is extremely uncommon to acquire a mature specimen, so even though they grow quickly, a 60cm tank should be sufficient until the fish reaches a total length of 40cm.

A secure lid is imperative for preventing escape. The young, which can wriggle out through cracks, require special vigilance. Since lungfishes need air to breath, there

A close-up of the head and anterior body of *Protopterus annectens* showing the sensory system. Photo by Edward C. Taylor.

must be ample space between the water surface and the lid.

FILTER SYSTEM:

The most desirable system is an exterior, pump-driven filter suited to the water volume. When the specimen gets big, it is suggested that a secondary system be added. The filter box should be wide and deep; ready-made filter systems should present no problems. Top filters should be of the accumulation style.

A word of warning for users of top filters: out of some perverse inclination, most species of lungfishes are known to wedge themselves between the pump intake tube and the tank wall, and if the pump is not tightly secured they will push it out of alignment so that water will be pumped onto the floor instead of into the tank, an unpleasant state of affairs. Filter systems for tanks of 75cm and up are secure enough, but in most smaller systems the pump sits on top of the filter box extension and is only secure within the box's frame. This type should be secured to the box with two-sided tape.

THERMOSTATS, HEATERS, ETC.:

The type of thermostat is not particularly important, but the way it is set up in the tank is. Lungfishes have sharp teeth and a strong bite, so it is not too difficult for them to break thermostats and heaters. Do not put this equipment unprotected into the tank, especially if the fish is large. The ideal thermostat is a typical bimetal type that can fit into the filter box. Other types should be firmly secured with rubber suction cups. The same goes for the heater. If it cannot fit into the filter box, use the convenient heater cover. This will not only protect it from the jaws of the lungfish, but prevent the none-too-bright lungfishes from getting burned. Finally, if a thermometer that can be put in the filter box and be seen from the outside is not available, avoid using the glass tube type. There is a variety of safer types on the market.

CARE:

Water Temperature and Conditions.– There is no need to be overly cautious about the water temperature; the standard tropical fish settings, around 24-26°C, are fine. *Protopterus* are known for inhabiting the very alkaline lakes of East Africa, but their distribution is actually primarily in the surrounding wetlands and tributaries on the delta. So both *Protopterus* and *Lepidosiren* should be kept at around pH 6.0-7.0, the pH of their primary habitats.

Food.–In the wild, *Protopterus* and *Lepidosiren* eat a variety of aquatic

A tank set up for the keeping of lungfishes.

life, primarily shellfish. In fact, in Lake Victoria they say that *P. aethiopicus* leaves a trail of broken shells. However, since I have no practical experience with them, I'll say nothing further. In captivity, though, fishes (goldfish and loaches), crustaceans (shrimp and krill, frozen

1) Sandbag weight. **2)** Lid leaves no gaps. **3)** Thermostat firmly secured with suction cups both at the bottom and the top. **4)** Small amount of bottom sand. **5)** Covered heater. **6)** Water level somewhat low. **7)** Thermometer attached to the window of the filter box.

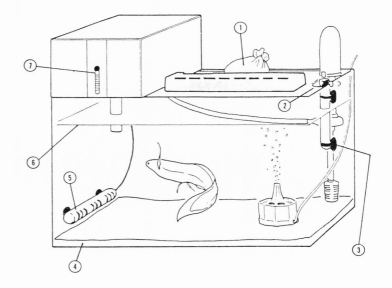

shrimp, etc.), and various meat or vegetable dry foods are enough for the lungfish's diet and have never to my knowledge led to any problems. Both genera are very small consumers of fishes in the wild, so if they have a habit of waiting for a while before they feed, it is not because they do not like the food, it is just their natural way of doing things (Greenwood, 1986). I have observed a *Protopterus* in captivity eating small fishes when it was hungry enough. Young eat frozen or live bloodworms, and if there is no bottom gravel for them to escape to, tubificid worms (Itomimizu) are good, too. As a general rule, the amount of food should be on the low side for both young and old; mature specimens don't even need daily feeding.

Water Changing.–Almost all damage to the extremely robust lungfishes is caused by poor water quality. The lungfish's peculiar "finicky" style of eating obviously leads to water pollution in the limited environment of the tank. In dirty water it may develop some or all of the following symptoms: white discharge from the eyes, sores on the skin, erosion of the tip of the fins and gills. These symptoms can be alleviated by frequent water changing at the first signs, but the underlying cause can lead to the death of the fish if these symptoms are neglected. With this in mind, the responsible aquarist will change some water at least once every ten days, changing ⅓ to ½ at a time. The filter box material should be cleaned once or twice a month.

Sickness.–Besides the injuries described above, burns from the

Protopterus annectens going up for air.

heater (which can be treated with tropical fish medicated balms available in stores), and reactions to dirty water, there are very few cases of regular sickness among lungfishes in captivity.

I'll mention a rare incident that must have taken place more than 10 years ago. Actually, there were two cases of the same strange condition, both afflicting *P. amphibius*. Both illnesses seemed to have been underway before we purchased them, and probably before they were even imported. First, there were round swellings on the body which eventually began to split open like pomegranates. We tried everything, but they didn't respond to treatment and the fish soon died. These are the only two cases of this I know of, and the only advice I can give is to check specimens for any sign of these swellings before buying them.

Other Cautions.–Young lungfishes should not be raised in a tank with an elaborate layout, at least not with potentially injurious driftwood or stones with sharp edges and points. Never forget about the powerful bite of the lungfish, and make sure young children cannot put their fingers near it.

REFERENCES:
    Bannister, K. E. 1987. *Coelacanth, Lungfish, and Polypterus.* K. E. Bannister, ed., Animal Encyclopedia, vol. 13: Fish. Heibonsha, Tokyo, 132-135.
    Boulenger, G. A. 1909. *Catalogue of the fresh-water fishes of Africa in the British Museum (Natural History).*

A *Protopterus amphibius* tamely takes food from the aquarist's hand.

The Australian Lungfish, *Neoceratodus forsteri*, is fully protected and may only be taken by special permit. In some juveniles the belly is a beautiful orange-pink color. Photo by Dr. Guido Dingerkus.

A small *Protopterus annectens* of about 18 cm length. The gills are still fully visible above the pectoral fins.

The yellow spotted pattern on the head and body of this *Lepidosiren paradoxus* normally will disappear with growth. Photo by Edward C. Taylor.

An albino *Protopterus aethiopicus* that was collected in the Stanley Pool. Albinos are not that rare and occasionally appear for sale, albeit at a higher price than the normally colored individuals. Photo by Edward C. Taylor.

British Museum (Natural History), Vol. 1, London. 373pp., 270figs.

Gosse, J.P. 1984. Protopteridae: *in* J. Daget, J.-P. Gosse & D.F.E. Thys van den Audenaerde, ed. *Check-list of the Freshwater Fishes of Africa. Vol. 1.* MRAC & ORSTOM, 8-17.

Greenwood, P.H. 1986. The Natural History of African Lungfishes. *Journ. Morphol., suppl. 1:*163-179.

Günther, A. 1870. *Catalogue of the fishes in the British Museum.* Vol. 8, London. 549pp.

Poll, M. 1961. Révision systématique et raciation géographique de Protopteridae de l'Afrique centrale. *Annals Mus. roy. Afr. cent.* 103:1-50, 6pls.

RAISING FRESHWATER RAYS

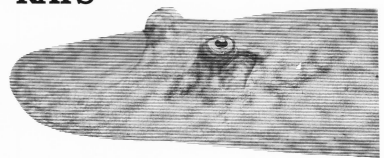

by Nobuhito Kuroiwa

The cartilaginous fishes, class Chondrichthys, which includes mainly sharks and rays, are believed to have appeared in the Devonian era. At the subclass level, these are divided into the elasmobranchs, holocephalans, xenacanths, and cladoselachians. The Holocephalans, including the chimaeras, are still extant, as are the elasmobranchs, which contains the sharks and rays. The other two subclasses are long extinct. The rays (order Rajiformes) are thought to be a derivative of the sharks because their gestation periods are similar.

Among the five known suborders of rays, the following families contain freshwater species: the Dasyatidae (stingrays), the closely related Potamotrygonidae (river stingrays), and the Pristidae (sawfishes), which are closely related to the sharks. Besides the Potamotrygonidae, which are distributed in South America and are imported for aquarium keeping, none of these families have species that are completely fresh water, although further research may reveal such species. But most of the species known at this point move between sea water and fresh water.

Cartilaginous fishes are known for their ability to use urea to adjust their permeability to salt water, but the proportion of urea in the body fluids of the completely freshwater species of the Potamotrygonidae is extremely small, which is why they cannot survive in salt water. Of this family, fourteen species in genus *Potamotrygon* and one species in genus *Disceus* are fresh water. At present, one genus of sixteen species of Dasyatidae, and one genus of six species of Pristidae are known to be able to live to a certain point in fresh

A sawfish must be handled with care. It is most closely related to sharks as can be seen by the body shape.

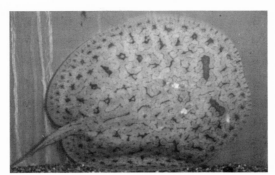
One of the short-tailed freshwater rays, *Disceus aiereba*.

water. All of the freshwater species grow fairly large. Species of the largest (in size) family, Pristidae, grow to seven meters.

MORPHOLOGY:

Rays are morphologically quite different from most tropical fishes raised in aquaria. Let's take a member of the family Potamotrygonidae as an example. Most of the body is composed of the disk, the round flat area that contains the head, trunk, and pectoral fins (which extend horizontally). On the underside of the disk there is a pair of nostrils and the mouth. Just behind the mouth are five pairs of gill slits, and farther toward the rear is the anus. On the sides of the anus are small pelvic fins, at the base of which are the male's sexual organs. On top of the disk are the eyes, and just behind them are two large spiracles. Along the dorsal line are one to three rows of highly poisonous serrated spines. Then the tail extends until the caudal fin at the end, except in the whip-like tail of some species of Dasyatidae which are not considered to have fins. Most species have some sort of spines that are composed of transformed scales and run from the base of the tail to the (big, singular) tail spine. Some species have a very rough and spiny back.

RANGE:

Freshwater rays are found in the large rivers of the world's tropical and subtropical zones.

The exclusively freshwater Potamotrygonidae is distributed widely in the waters of South America, including the Amazon, La Plata, and Orinoco River systems. We know of 11 species that are from the Amazon and La Plata Rivers, and 6 that are native to the Orinoco. About half of these species are limited to their systems, and half are able to range outside them. For example, the most popular species for aquarium keeping and raising, *Potamotrygon hystrix*, occurs in all three systems. The second most popular species, *P. motoro*, is distributed in the Amazon and La Plata Rivers. The rivers that these and most other South American species occur in determine their colors, and the color and pattern variations among imports are quite amazing. This is the reason for the tremendous ray mania, but it makes it very hard for researchers to identify species, especially when the pertinent literature is so hard to acquire.

Freshwater species of Dasyatidae have been found in the Mekong and Menam Rivers of Southeast Asia, the Ganges River in India, and the Niger River in Africa. One that is imported from time to time is the Leopard Stingray of Southeast Asia (*Dasyatis bleekeri*). Other species appear very rarely.

The Pristidae also range widely in tropical and subtropical zones. *Pristis*

Anatomical features of rays:
Dorsal view: 1) Rostrum. **2)** Eyes. **3)** Spiracles. **4)** Disc. **5)** Pectoral fins. **6)** Dorsal tubercles. **7)** Poisonous spine. **8)** Ventral fins. **9)** Caudal fin. **Ventral view: 1)** Nostrils. **2)** Mouth. **3)** Five pairs of gill slits. **4)** Ventral fins. **5)** Claspers (in male). **6)** Anus.

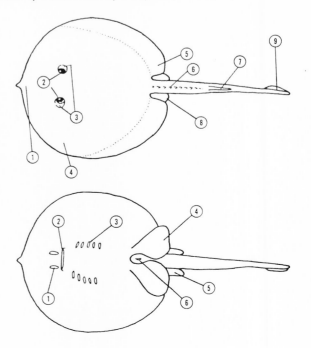

The underside of a sawfish, *Pristes pristes*. This is a strange sight indeed.

Two sawfishes (*Pristes pristes*). The teeth on the "saw" can cause a great deal of damage when swung back and forth, both to prey fishes and humans that are careless.

Potamotrygon hystrix.

Potamotrygon hystrix.

Potamotrygon motoro.

Potamotrygon motoro.

Potamotrygon reticulatus.

Potamotrygon reticulatus.

Potamotrygon motoro.

Potamotrygon hystrix.

137

perrotteti (said to be a synonym of *P. microdon*) is a well-traveled species, found in the Gambia and Zambezi Rivers in Africa, parts of Florida and the Gulf of Mexico, and in South America to Brazil. Another species ranging from North America south through Brazil is *P. pectinata*. The former species reaches lengths of 3 meters, and the latter up to 5.5 meters. *P. microdon* ranges around Indonesia, New Guinea, and Australia, and has been imported in the past in small numbers. This species also attains lengths of about 5 meters. I do not know details about the remaining three species.

BEHAVIOR:

Many aspects of the behavior of freshwater rays are still puzzling. Although the habitats of the Potamotrygonidae and Dasyatidae are different, the behavior of members of the two families is thought to be similar. They share certain morphological characteristics, such as the poisonous tail spines, and both are naturally feared by the native peoples of their habitats. Although the stingray's sting is not fatal, it is extremely painful. The swelling and pain are said to last as long as a week in some cases. The spines are barbed and consequently hard to remove. According to my observations of a captive specimen, the spines fall off every two to three months to be replaced by fresh ones. They do not all fall off at the same time, so there is always a defense mechanism in place. The spines grow with the individual— the spines of a *P. motoro* with a disk diameter of 45cm can be as long as 6cm.

Species of Dasyatidae generally live on the bottom sand, often hiding by half burying themselves. They can swim fast when frightened or pursuing prey. Species of Potamotrygonidae generally occur in clear running water, and they are nocturnal by nature. In the day they stay in relatively deep waters, and move to shallow waters at night to catch sleeping fishes. After eating they bury themselves in the sand (like the Dasyatidae) to rest until the sun starts to rise and they then head for deeper water. Locals can tell where rays live from the traces of these holes they make in the sand.

All cartilaginous fishes are carnivorous. The stingrays have a very strong bite, and feed mostly on shellfish, shrimp, and crabs. The Potamotrygonidae probably have the same mouth structure but their diet differs somewhat in that they are thought to eat a greater proportion of small fishes, such as characins. The fascinating hunting style of these rays

Top: A ray in its natural habitat, on the bottom of a South American river. **Bottom:** A close view of the poisonous tail spine.

can be observed in the tank. The ray slowly and nonchalantly nears the prey until it is close enough to suddenly pounce and cover it with its disk. Then it uses its fins to get it in contact with its mouth.

The species of the family Pristidae have a different method. They swim into a school of fish and thrash their saw-like snout around until it kills something. They also use this saw or sword in self defense and for digging holes.

All species of cartilaginous fishes are internal egg fertilizers, and not all rays, but the three freshwater families described here, are ovoviviparous. That is, the oviduct changes to act as a uterus where the eggs are stored until they are ready to hatch. The new young usually live off a yolk sac. It is said that the Pristidae has its saw-like snout from the time of hatching. The number of young born at one time is limited to about 12 for all these families. This is about all that can be said with any confidence about the behavior of these families.

RAISING RAYS:

Most aquarists are very familiar with the primitive fishes we have described, such as the bichirs and lungfishes, but people with no interest in raising tropical fishes may have never even heard of them. Even though everyone has heard of rays and sharks, few know anything about these freshwater rays. They can be raised right in a freshwater tank with your other tropical fishes! They make a strange and attractive addition to any aquarist's collection. Everything about them is different from the aquarist's previous experience: the way they swim, feed, everything! They become so tame that they will readily take food from your hand. I had a ray that grew to a disc diameter of 50 cm in three years that I would feed by hand. After I removed the tank lid, it would creep along the

Ventral view of a ray as it adheres to the front aquarium glass.

wall it was "stuck" to, making sucking noises and basically begging for its food. I would hold out the food and let it crawl onto my hand. When I let go of the food, the ray would skillfully guide it to its mouth and eat it. This is a great trick to show your friends.

Recently, a greater variety of species of Potamotrygonidae have been imported, due to increased transportation methods and a widened collecting range. There is such variety in the body coloring that there are truly no two alike. When I see how incredibly beautiful some species are, and how specimen after specimen has its own unique beauty, I am once again blown away by the immense diversity of South American fishes.

Except for some unusual species, raising rays will not be difficult for the conscientious aquarist who learns the rules. I will now lay out the basic guidelines for raising the relatively available, completely freshwater species of the family Potamotrygonidae. Then there will be a brief description of raising species of the family Dasyatidae, which are difficult to keep a long time because they need some salt in their water. I will omit Pristidae because it grows so large that few individuals can consider keeping it outside of public or research aquariums.

RAISING FRESHWATER STINGRAYS (POTAMOTRYGONIDAE)

Tank: Some large rays will, under good living conditions, grow unexpectedly quickly, soon outgrowing even a 180cm tank. Most imported rays are young, so a lot of further

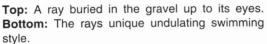

Top: A ray buried in the gravel up to its eyes.
Bottom: The rays unique undulating swimming style.

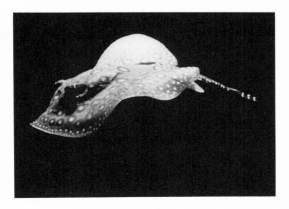

139

growth has to be taken into consideration. The area of the tank bottom is the priority for rays, and the tank should also be high enough to allow them to easily "stand up" and cling to the walls. Finally, the tank should hold a decent volume of water because rays are very sensitive to changes in water conditions, and the greater the volume the more gradual changes will be.

Of course, this does not mean turning the basement into an aquarium. Here are some figures: *P. hystrix* and *P. motoro* would do well in a 120 X 45 X 60cm tank. A small specimen with a diameter of 20cm or less will do fine in a 60cm tank, but it is best to start out with a bigger tank to account for future growth. I started out with a specimen that grew quite large in a 120cm tank, and then moved it to a 180cm tank with good results.

Of course, once a specimen gets used to a tank, it is best to avoid the trauma of moving it. Even a tank kept under the same system is risky. There are too many factors—other species, their size and number, frequency and amount of water changes, etc.—to hope that the water conditions will be very equal. Once I decided to renovate a 180cm tank in which I kept a ray that I had brought back myself from South America, so I moved it into a prepared 120cm tank. In 5 minutes it was dead. The 120cm tank even had half of its water from the 180cm tank; the other fish showed no signs of any trouble. The sensitivity of rays cannot be overstressed. If transfer is necessary, at least attempt to get the pH levels exactly or near exactly the same.

COHABITATION:

Fishes that are roughly the same size and are upper strata swimmers, like arowanas and gars, are no problem. Middle and bottom swimmers should be relatively mild-mannered and big, like the Tiger Shovelnose Catfish or *Polypterus*. Whether it is because of the fearful stingers or the unusual shape, rays are rarely attacked. Rays and other fishes in the tank usually ignore each other. However, curious fishes such as large American cichlids or Red-tailed Catfish, and other aggressive, nosy fishes, will cause trouble. When a ray gets big it may catch even large fishes

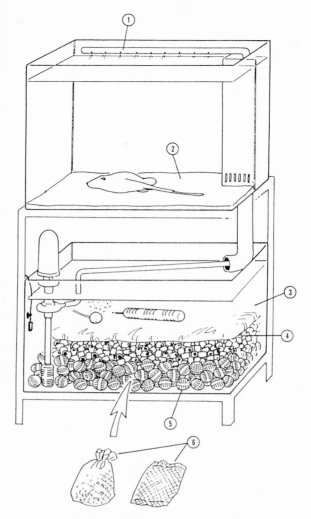

1) A gentle spray of water. **2)** A thin layer of sand. **3)** Floss (wool) mat. **4)** Ceramic filter material. **5)** Bio-balls. **6)** Bags of activated charcoal and coral as needed.

like *Polypterus* under its disc, but not to worry, for it will release them as soon as it realizes there is no way it can fit them into its mouth. Unlike most fishes, the ray cannot open its mouth very widely at all, and it cannot swallow anything wider than its bite. Rays are fine with other rays; it is thought that even specimens of very different sizes will not fight or eat each other.

The only other consideration is food: rays are not as agile hunters as other fishes, or at least not as fast. They should not be kept with fast-feeding fishes, or you should limit the number of fishes so that enough food gets to the ray.

FILTERS, HEATERS, AND OTHER EQUIPMENT:

The filter system used in a ray tank

Potamotrygon hystrix. Some rays will almost blend in with their surroundings. In fact, they will cover themselves up to their eyes in bottom material (usually sand) to hide.

should be especially strong. Generally, a top or exterior filter is used, but again these should be stronger than the usual system. The most desirable system is the overflow type used in saltwater tanks. Since the filter box is placed under the tank, it allows for a larger, markedly more effective system. It also makes obtrusive hoses and pumps in the tank obsolete.

Either a thin layer of sand should be spread on the bottom or there should be no sand at all. If the layer of sand is too thick, waste products will accumulate in it, resulting in an increase of harmful ammonia and nitrite concentrations. The ray will suffer congestion in its white underbelly from burrowing in this polluted sand. If the sand is shallow enough, the ray cannot bury itself in it. A large proportion of the ray's body comes in contact with the bottom of the tank, and its skin is very delicate. It is too bad that the ray cannot enjoy its natural habit of burrowing in the sand in an aquarium, but aquaria cannot imitate the Amazon habitat closely enough.

The pump should be strong, but the inflow should be adjusted so that it creates a mild current. The water should be aerated sufficiently, since the ray prefers water with a high oxygen content. The filter box should have non-clogging polyethylene bioballs, with macaroni-shaped, porous ceramic filter material in it as well, and a wool mat on top. This set-up will last a long time without clogging or becoming stopped up, maintaining a good environment for digestive bacteria. In reaction to pH changes, activated charcoal, large-granule coral sand, or calcareous filter sand can be used for readjustments.

The most important thing in the tank is a broad area for the ray to move around in, so an elaborate layout should not be created. The heater must be covered and secured to an out-of-the-way part of the aquarium wall if it cannot be set up in the filter box. The heater should never be put in the sand where the ray could get burned.

MANAGING WATER CONDITIONS :

This may be the most important aspect of raising a ray. Generally, the

pH should be kept in the range of 6.5-7.2, and the water temperature for Amazonian species at 24-27°C and for La Plata species at 23-25°C.

Ammonia and nitrites damage fish's respiratory organs, as most aquarists know, but the ray is especially susceptible to these effects because it has no natural immunity to them. To prevent any accumulation of these pollutants, very frequent small-volume water changes should be made. It depends on the filter power, but as a general rule changing one-fourth of the tank volume once a week should keep the ray healthy. Changing more than

A ray has trapped a small fish and is moving it toward its mouth.

one-third of the volume at one time will probably change the chemistry of the water enough to cause stress in the ray.

A ray that has been kept a long time has probably grown so used to the water that water straight from the tap can be used as long as only one-fourth of the tank is changed and it is at the same temperature and pH as that of the tank water. However, with a recently imported specimen the water should not be direct from the tap but allowed to sit for a while ("pre-drawn water"). If it must be direct from the tap, only one-fifth or less volume should be changed, and neutralizers should be added immediately. The filter box should be cleaned once a month, and the wool mat washed lightly at that time. A healthy ray normally eats a lot and moves around a lot, clings vertically to the glass wall, and makes sucking noises. If it is getting sick from bad water, it will start neglecting food and spend a lot of time motionless on the bottom. The color of its underbelly is also a good indicator of health: bright white is healthy, slightly colored is a warning sign, and red is seriously ill. The ray should be observed carefully and consistently; problems often seem to occur after the aquarist has had the ray for some time and starts to get lax in his or her observations.

ILLNESSES:

It is often difficult to tell whether an unhealthy ray is suffering from poor water conditions or some sort of illness, and too many of them die without this question being satisfactorily answered. Besides these sudden deaths, more chronic conditions to watch out for include

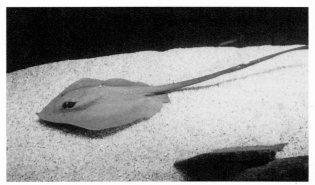

Most dasyatids are not completely freshwater animals and need a brackish system.

burns from the heater, injuries from other fishes, and chafing around the spines, which could lead to a cotton-like fungus developing on the sores. These conditions can be alleviated with medicines available from your local pet shop, like Green F Gold, but again the sensitivity of rays calls for mild dosages of any medicine at first, with slight increases if no negative reactions are indicated.

FOOD:

Live small fishes and shrimp are a ray's favorite foods. It is a really big eater for having such a thin body. A 50cm disc ray can easily eat 5 or 6 fish of 5cm length in a meal. Its disc swells up visibly after a meal, and I usually feed mine once the swelling has gone back down and the stomach is clearly empty again.

When live foods are hard to obtain, frozen shrimp (Muki-shrimp) and fish fillets are good, but they should be as fresh and as good quality (no frost) as possible because oxidized fats are harmful to fishes. The shrimp should be non-salted because the ray will not eat salty foods. Krill and processed (artificial) foods are possibilities, but once a specimen has gotten used to live food it is very difficult to get it to eat anything else. Processed alternatives also will contribute to poor water quality. As always, any leftovers should be removed from the tank as soon as possible. Finally, young rays with disc diameters of 20cm or less are fed bloodworms, killifishes, and tubificid worms, and gradually switched to other foods as they grow.

ACQUISITION:

There are some things aquarists need to especially watch out for when purchasing a ray. Many rays in shop tanks are in bad shape from the trauma of being transported from their natural habitats. If the ray has not been kept in good conditions in a shop for about a month, you should reserve one and give it a week or two to calm down and recover from the trip before taking it home. This will also give you time to adjust the water conditions in your home tank. It is always best to go to a shop that has handled rays for a while even if they are relatively expensive: a cheap specimen that dies quickly is no bargain. Check for the signs of health described above. It is a good idea to ask the clerk to feed the ray in front of you. A healthy ray will immediately notice the food and go after it energetically. Specimens with missing fins or tails lopped off halfway are not uncommon, and these injuries do not always heal perfectly. One such specimen of mine had a fin with a bite taken out of it that grew back to its original shape, but the pattern didn't exactly fit. This sort of injury is unrelated to its health, though.

BREEDING:

Rays fertilize internally and are ovoviviparous—they have sexual intercourse and give birth to live young. Pregnant fish have been imported to give birth here in Japan. Rays have been successfully bred in captivity in large aquariums. Males and females can be easily distinguished by their sex organs, which are located at the base of the pectoral fins. Healthy specimens may be easy to breed, but rays have been

143

imported in large numbers only recently. We expect to hear more about home aquarists' experiences with breeding in the near future. I am looking forward to raising a pair, then hopefully a family, soon.

RAISING DASYATIDAE:

Unfortunately, species of the family Dasyatidae are as difficult to keep for a long time as they are beautiful. Unlike the Potamotrygonidae, most species are not completely freshwater animals. Therefore, they have to be raised in water that is at least 50% salt water, and the system should be the same as that for any seawater aquarium. Some species have very long tails and so the tanks should be correspondingly larger.

REFERENCES:

Berra, T. M. 1981. *An Atlas of Distribution of the Freshwater Families of the World.* Univ. of Nebraska Press.

Dingerkus, G. 1987. Rays and Sharks ("gin-zame") *in* K. E. Bannister, ed., Iwai Tamotsu, Chief Editor. *Animal Encyclopedia*, 13th Edition. Fish. Heibon-sha. pp146-151.

Kimura, Shige. 1983. *Sakana Shinshi-Roku (A Who's Who of Fish).* Midori Shobo.

Matsusaka, Makoto. 1991. *Freshwater Stingrays.* Aqua Magazine. Fairwind.

Matsusaka, Makoto, et al. 1987. *Freshwater Ray Catalog.* Aqualife, 1987. 12. Marine Planning.

Nikolsky, G. V. 1982. *Ichthyological Taxonomy.* Third Edition, Revised and Enlarged, translated by Takai Akihiro. Tatara Shobo.

Taniuchi, Toru. 1987. *Potamotrygon. Fish Magazine*, 1987:4. Midori Shobo.

Uchida, Kiyoshi. 1963. *Animal Taxonomy 9: (I) Vertebrates: (1a) Fish.* Nakayama Shoten

AUTHORS

(IN ALPHABETICAL ORDER)

Igarashi, Toshiaki. Born in Tokyo in 1958. Known for being the first researcher of *Polypterus* in Japan. His main interests are in taxonomy. Earns an income of 0.5 to 1 million yen per year from publications. In 1988, he made a crucial contribution to the field by heroically bringing back scientific specimens from southern Ethiopia. His present research is in southern Sudan and southern Zaire.

Kuroiwa, Nobuhito. Born in 1962. Graduated Tokyo Nogyo University's Agriculture Dept. with a degree in landscape gardening. Now employed with Pleck Research Center, a private research concern. For ten years he has been interested in primitive fishes as a sideline to his plant research. He has travelled to South America, Southeast Asia, and Africa on fish collecting expeditions.

Kodera, Haruto. Born in Kyoto in 1948. Graduate of the Veterinary College of Nihon University. Presently a lecturer in the Dissection Laboratory of the Dental College of Tsurugami University. Specialist in comparative vertebrate dissection. Author of many works on evolution and anatomy.

Maeda, Hiroshi. Born in 1963. Graduated with a degree in Social Welfare from the Literature Dept. of Jochi University. Employed with the Toribane Aquarium's Planning Dept., where he is involved in public relations, translation of literature, and children's educational programs. He also travels overseas to make films.

Mitani, Shinya. Born in 1967. Graduated Mitsue University's Fisheries Department. Employed in Toribane Aquarium's Research Dept. He specializes in JUGON, freshwater fishes, insects, and amphibians. Reputedly able to talk to frogs.

Mori, Fumitoshi. Born June 16, 1958. Graduated with a major in Fisheries from the Veterinary College of Nihon University. After working for the Photo Library he became a photographer specializing in photos of reproductive behavior and imported fishes. He is an experienced tropical fish aquarist, and he has written for *Aqualife* and other publications. He has also written several books, including *Brand New Discus*.

Yamazaki, Koichi. Born in Tokyo in 1962. An animal and fish enthusiast since junior high school, he eschews categories like "tropical fishes" or "Japanese freshwater fishes," and prefers to simply raise and observe freshwater fishes that he likes. Presently employed with Sato Bosai Setsubi, a disaster prevention services company. He is a third dan karate expert.

Uchiyama, Ryu. Born in Tokyo in 1962. Graduated with a degree in Fisheries from the Oceanology Dept. of Tokai University. After serving an apprenticeship with photographer Kiyoshi Sakurai, he went free-lance. He has published many nature photos of fishing scenes, etc., in such publications as *Aqualife*. He has published several books as well, and he frequently travels abroad for his work.

INDEX